How to Use Sugar and Lose Weight

How to Use Sugar and Lose Weight

June Roth

INFORMATION, INCORPORATED
NEW YORK, N.Y.

© Copyright 1969 by June Roth
Printed in the United States of America
How to Use Sugar
and Lose Weight
Published by Information, Incorporated
New York, N.Y.

To Mother and Dad,
with
Many Sweet Thoughts Always

Rumor, misunderstandings and misstatements have all conspired to give sugar a bad name. This excellent book by June Roth, an excellent and thoughtful cook, should repair some of the damage. Sugar is one of the basic foods and need not be avoided for either weight control or healthy living.

Too many individuals don't realize that the powerful chemicals of our body can easily transform anything, yes anything, we eat to sugar—or to fat. If you need energy your body will transform foods into sugar. If you don't need energy it will store them as fat. These transformations are not an easy thing for the body to do; they often place a great strain upon the body. This is particularly true when people eat high protein diets. They place an extra burden on their kidneys, liver and other organs to transform these chemicals into the needed sugars and fat.

Every medical practitioner knows well that people will only stay with a diet they can enjoy. With this book as your guide you can have a most enjoyable, healthy and delicious life.

CLEMENT G. MARTIN, M.D.
Hillsdale, N.J.
Sept. 1969

DEAR DIETER:

Why fight the "losing battle" armed with half-truths and diet misconceptions? Don't do it!

What good is a svelte figure surrounding a nasty, sugar-starved disposition? Not worth it!

Can one cut down on calories, dine with satisfaction, and remain sweet-tempered? Yes, yes!

Here is a cookbook that has the answers. It will tickle your palate and permit you to gauge your calorie intake easily. It has been designed for the dieters who feel the need of sugar in their diet, who have a gourmet's desire for interesting food, and who have been hungry throughout every well-intentioned diet they have ever tried.

Recipes are clearly portion-controlled and calorie counts are given for each portion. I have spared no effort in designing low-calorie recipes that will let your sweet tooth have its fling while you do battle with the bulges.

Sincerely yours,
JUNE ROTH

CONTENTS

1. Lucky Losers 1
2. Sugar Sense 3
3. Mental Push-Ups 5
4. Trim Tempters 7
5. Skinny Soups 15
6. Melting Mainstays 23
7. Vain Vegetables 49
8. Slender Salads 65
9. Educated Eggs 79
10. Slim Sandwiches 85
11. Deft Desserts 91
12. Controlled Cakes 101
13. General Calorie Counts 109
14. Three Weeks of Delicious Dining for Less than 1000 Calories Daily 125

CHAPTER 1

LUCKY LOSERS

The only time when being a LOSER means you are a WINNER is when you are playing the diet game. The more you lose, the more you win, in good health, good looks and good sense.

If you are one of those people who cannot tolerate sugar substitutes, or who do not choose to use them, can you have any hope for losing weight? If you have decided that there are dangers lurking in the indiscriminate use of diet pills, and you need a crutch to bolster your wavering will power, can you reduce without them? If you are not a food chemist, will you ever be able to understand the technical aspects of selecting your menus wisely?

Yes! If you are intelligent, overweight and slim-thinking, you can stop insulting your body with fad diets. If you really care about your health and appearance, and you do not want to take a diet pill ever again, or fight fat ever again, there is a way to get off the gaining-and-losing seesaw once and for all time. Habitual overeating is a conditioned reflex that must be retrained, so peel pounds the sensible way by using your brain first!

Learn the facts of fat. Obesity is caused by an excess intake of calories. Each excess pound of stored fat on your body represents 3500 calories of unneeded energy, that has not been spent. To lose that one pound in a week, you must consume 3500 calories LESS than your usual weekly intake. To lose two pounds, a sensible goal, you must consume 7000 calories LESS. This amounts to 1000 calories LESS EACH DAY.

A calorie is a unit of energy that fuels your body, burning up as your heart beats, as you breathe, as you expend energy on activities. The average person needs about one million calories a year to function properly, and that is a lot of delicious dining if your menus are selected with care.

The obese are not hungrier than everyone else. Their problem seems to be an inability to stop eating, and they are conditioned to eating even in the absence of hunger sensations. Their appestats (appetite control centers) need retraining, and scientists suggest that the obese are probably suffering from abnormalities in satiety rather than abnormalities in hunger.

If satisfaction is the problem, then it is also the cause of failure in most diets. Food is a source of pleasure to overweight people, and because they love to eat they will not put up with stingy dining very long. The challenge is to provide meals that are well-balanced, low-in-calories, and temptingly satisfying and delicious. The ingredients must be chosen wisely, the seasonings cleverly, and the offerings must have a gourmet touch. It has to be a worthwhile experience, and at the same time a retraining experience to prove that satisfaction does not need to come from quantity but rather from quality.

Let your doctor help you determine exactly what your calorie intake should be, considering your occupation, your gender and your size. Then let me help you, with this book, to realize that dieting can be an adventure in eating well, and that you need not give up the sweet and necessary energy of sugar to accomplish a loss of weight.

Photo courtesy of Nestle Company

Applesauce Meringue (page 107)
Photo courtesy of the S&W Company

CHAPTER 2

SUGAR SENSE

It is foolish to make sugar the culprit for overeating and bad food choices. At a mere 18 calories a teaspoonful, it is an effective energy producer, taste improver, and will raise your blood sugar level faster than any other food. When your blood sugar level is low, your appestat registers "hungry," and you are apt to eat more than you need before your blood sugar level can rise again. So a bit of sugar before you eat can actually curb your appetite during the meal that follows.

The purpose of this book is to give a variety of recipes using small amounts of natural sugar in all forms. They are designed to be long on taste and short on calories, and should be proof that where there is the will there is the way to enjoy dieting. Eliminating 1000 calories from your daily diet to effect a two-pound weekly loss, and still feel hunger satisfaction, requires major rethinking about your intake. It also requires understanding about the most elementary aspects of nutrition. All food falls into the categories of protein, fats and carbohydrates.

We consume carbohydrates chiefly in the form of sugar and starch. In a test reported in Nutrition News (April, 1964) a research team set out to discover what happened when dieters ate meals with plenty of proteins and fats but with no carbohydrates. The article reported that it made little difference if the dieters were getting 1500 or 2000 calories a day of the protein-fat diets; with all carbohydrates excluded the subjects showed signs of starvation. When carbohydrates were returned to the daily diet, the abnormalities began to return toward normal. Thus, although a weight loss was shown, it was not regarded to be a safe and sensible weight loss, because the cost may be far higher than the dieter may realize.

An important aspect in understanding carbohydrates' importance in creating energy is to know that proteins give just as much energy. The body needs energy to stay alive, and that is the first concern. If protein is the only energy source of nutrient, it will be used for that purpose, rather than for its essential purpose for building cells, for hemoglobin, for antibodies, and for the fluid balance of the body. When carbohydrates are on hand to take care of the body's energy needs, protein is available for its own special uses in the body. You can readily see that a well-balanced diet intake, low-calorie though it may be, is the logical plan for continued well being.

The recipes in this book offer you the use of small amounts of natural sugar in your diet, suggesting portion-controlled and calorie-controlled recipes to suit every menu need. It puts you in control of choosing and maintaining a sensible and reasonable method of dieting with permanent results. Every recipe carefully tells you the number of portions and the calorie count of each portion. Simple addition will trim the excess upholstery from your svelte and healthy body, releasing the REAL YOU from that fat padded prison of the overweight!

CHAPTER 3
MENTAL PUSH-UPS

Flex your mental muscles and think seriously about what you hope to achieve in reshaping your appearance and your health. Be realistic about expected weight losses. The unspent calories were put in your fat bank slowly and will take time to deplete.

The first week of dieting may reveal a large loss, thereafter two pounds a week should be a good schedule. If you hit a weight plateau, after conscientious regimen, don't be discouraged. The cells, having released excess fat, fill up with water many times before releasing that too. Spare the salt shaker to prevent this water retention and you will soon see the expected weight loss. Your instinct may be to curtail your intake of water if this plateau occurs. Don't! Drink six to eight glasses of fluid a day, counting water, tea or coffee, and help nature to flush the pounds away.

When faced with dining out, learn to analyze the portion on your plate and decide immediately what you are going to leave. If you are in a position to order your meal, be judicious in your selection of lower-calorie foods. Remember that you are on a program of subtracting not adding to your fat reserve system.

Everywhere you go, people are talking about dieting. Don't join them for a while. Change the subject. Don't call attention to what you are doing. Indeed, it would be wise to find a brand-new interest and embark on it at the same time as your diet. If your problem isn't hunger of the body, it may be caused by hunger of the intellect. Feed your mind during this period instead!

If you are used to sugaring your coffee, cut it down half a teaspoon at a time, until you reach the point where your beverage is still enjoyable. Many people can gradually work their way down from an accustomed two teaspoons to a mere half teaspoonful. If this gives you pleasure, and no aftertaste, then you are entitled to enjoy the few calories it costs. The object is to investigate and subtract large areas of calories from your habitual way of eating, to still enjoy dining by trading your usual menu for an equally delicious one, and not to pick on the tiny luxuries. Ever watch a dieter pop a sweetening pill into coffee and then order nesselrode pie? Rather to pop the sugar in and keep the dessert reasonable too!

Remember if you want to get off this treadmill of dieting once and for all, you will have to maintain your weight loss for at least six months, to give your body a chance to stabilize at the new weight. Thereafter, never let a few pounds become ten and twenty—ditch those few pounds before they begin to surround you with another wall of fat!

Dieters are people who have one sure thing in common, they love to eat. The recipes throughout this book pay attention to that fact, and you will find tantalizing dishes from which to choose your menus. A wide range of seasonings will expand your taste horizons as it contracts your waistline!

Shrimp Deluxe Salad (page 71)
Photo courtesy of the Green Giant Company

Shrimp Kabobs (page 14)
Photo courtesy of the Florida Citrus Commission

CHAPTER 4

TRIM TEMPTERS

Every little nibble has a meaning all its own. Make sure that what you nibble adds to your satisfaction as you chalk it up against your calorie count each day. Enjoy the luxury of real meals when you diet, and the pleasure that a variety of courses will bring.

Here are a group of no-account nibbles, a bargain in taste satisfaction that leaves room for several courses to follow. A sweet start to losing weight!

BANANA AMBROSIA

3 oranges
2 bananas
1 teaspoon powdered sugar
1 ounce dried coconut

Peel orange and cut into thin discs. Then cut the discs in quarters. Peel and slice bananas. Combine the two, and stir lightly with powdered sugar. Spoon into sherbet glasses and top with a pinch of coconut.
Serves 8. About 68 calories per serving.

BROILED GRAPEFRUIT

2 grapefruits, halved
4 teaspoons brown sugar
1 teaspoon cinnamon

Cut around segments of halves of grapefruit. Sprinkle top of each half with a teaspoon of brown sugar and a dash or two of cinnamon. Broil grapefruit for about 6 minutes, or until browned. Serve hot.
Serves 4. About 63 calories per serving.

STRAWBERRY-MELON COCKTAIL

3 cups cantaloupe melon balls
1 cup sliced strawberries
1 tablespoon powdered sugar
4 sprigs of mint

Combine melon balls and sliced strawberries. Sprinkle with powdered sugar and mix through gently. Let stand for an hour in the refrigerator until well chilled. Divide into four sherbet glasses. Garnish with a sprig of mint.
Serves 4. About 39 calories per serving.

CHEESE PUFFS

18 *saltine crackers*
2 *tablespoons salad dressing, mayonnaise type*
2 *tablespoons sour cream*
2 *tablespoons grated onion*

1 *teaspoon soy sauce*
2 *tablespoons grated Parmesan cheese*
1 *stiffly-beaten egg white*

Arrange crackers on a cookie sheet. Combine salad dressing, sour cream, onion, soy sauce, and Parmesan cheese. Fold stiffly-beaten egg white into the mixture. Spread on crackers and bake for 10 minutes at 450 degrees, or until lightly browned. Makes 1½ dozen canapes. About 28 calories each.

CRAB CANAPES

30 *saltine crackers*
1 *cup shredded crabmeat, canned*
½ *cup condensed cream of celery soup, canned*
2 *tablespoons sherry*

1 *tablespoon finely chopped pimiento*
1 *teaspoon Worcestershire sauce*
3 *tablespoons fine bread crumbs*

Arrange saltines on a flat cookie sheet. Combine crabmeat with undiluted celery soup. Add sherry, pimiento, and Worcestershire sauce. Spoon onto crackers. Top with bread crumbs. Slip under the broiler for 3 minutes, or until crumbs are brown. Serve at once.
Makes 2½ dozen canapes. About 26 calories each.

RAW VEGETABLE DIP

1 cup sour cream
1 teaspoon onion powder
1 teaspoon salt
¼ teaspoon monosodium
    glutamate

½ teaspoon grated lemon peel
1½ tablespoons fresh
    lemon juice
¼ teaspoon soy sauce
½ teaspoon sugar

In a small mixing bowl beat sour cream on low speed until light and fluffy. Add remaining ingredients, blending well. Refrigerate. Before serving, stir to creamy consistency. Makes about 1 cup of sauce. Arrange a platter of fresh cauliflower flowerets, carrot sticks, cucumber spears, and other suitable raw, crisp vegetables. Keep chilled until ready to serve. Place sauce in the center of the platter.
Sauce is about 9 calories per teaspoon.

SMOKED SALMON-CUCUMBER STICKS

½ pound smoked salmon,
    sliced thin
2 cucumbers

3 tablespoons sour cream
1 tablespoon grated onion
½ teaspoon sugar

Cut salmon into long thin strips. Peel cucumbers and cut each lengthwise into eight strips; then cut across in thirds. Blend grated onion and sugar into sour cream. Spread each strip of salmon with sour cream mixture; then wrap around a cucumber strip with sour cream mixture against the cucumber. Arrange on a platter with picks.
Makes about 48 appetizers. About 10 calories each.

COCKTAIL FRANKS IN ZESTY SAUCE

6 all-beef frankfurters
⅓ cup hickory catsup
2 tablespoons fresh
   lemon juice
½ cup water

½ teaspoon
   Worcestershire sauce
½ teaspoon salt
⅛ teaspoon pepper
½ teaspoon horseradish
¼ cup parsley

    Boil or broil frankfurters and cut each into 6 small sections. Spear with toothpicks and serve with the following sauce: Combine hickory catsup, lemon juice, water, Worcestershire sauce, salt and pepper in a saucepan. Simmer over medium heat, stirring occasionally, until mixture is thick, about 7 minutes. Chill. Just before serving, stir in horseradish and parsley. Makes about ⅔ cup of sauce.

Makes 36 hors d'oeuvres. About 28 calories each, with sauce. Sauce alone, is about 9 calories per tablespoon, and may be used with shrimp or meatballs with equal taste satisfaction.

COCKTAIL ONION APPETIZERS

1 jar (15 ounces)
   cocktail onions
½ cup sour cream

1 teaspoon brown sugar
¼ cup snipped fresh parsley
1 tablespoon paprika

    Spear onions on wooden picks; dip in sour cream in which brown sugar has been thoroughly blended. Then dip in parsley or in paprika, making some green and some red. Arrange on a platter or stick into a whole fresh grapefruit.
About 2 calories each.

SALTINE PIZZAS

1 can condensed
  tomato soup, undiluted
½ teaspoon oregano
½ teaspoon sugar

1 teaspoon lemon juice
4 dozen saltine crackers
¼ cup grated Parmesan cheese

    Combine soup, oregano, sugar, and lemon juice. Spread on each of 4 dozen saltine crackers. Sprinkle with grated Parmesan cheese. Bake in 400 degree oven for 4 minutes, or until cheese melts. Serve at once.
Makes 4 dozen appetizers. About 20 calories each.

ORANGE FREEZE

4 medium oranges
½ cup fresh orange juice

1 bottle (12-ounces)
  lemon-lime carbonated
  beverage

    Peel oranges; slice into cartwheels. Chill. Combine orange juice and carbonated beverage; pour into shallow pan and place in freezer. Freeze until crystals form on bottom of pan. Stir mixture and continue to freeze until partially frozen and slushy. Quickly transfer to a chilled bowl and whip with electric beater at high speed until smooth. (Or place into electric blender; cover and blend at high speed until smooth). Spoon into serving dishes and top with orange slices. Serve at once. Garnish with fresh mint if desired.
Serves 8. About 57 calories per serving.

SAVORY STUFFED MUSHROOMS

24 large fresh mushrooms
½ cup cottage cheese
½ teaspoon garlic salt
1 tablespoon chopped chives
¼ teaspoon Worcestershire sauce
¼ teaspoon thyme
½ teaspoon brown sugar
½ teaspoon paprika

Wash mushrooms; remove stems and reserve for use in another dish. Cover mushroom caps with salted water and boil in covered saucepan about 15 minutes. Drain; chill. Combine remaining ingredients, except paprika and spoon into mushroom caps. Sprinkle with paprika. Serve chilled. Makes 24 appetizers. About 9 calories each.

CUCUMBER-EGG WAFERS

1 long firm cucumber
2 hard boiled eggs
1 tablespoon chopped chives
1 tablespoon sour cream
½ teaspoon sugar
Dash of Worcestershire sauce

Peel cucumber and run the tines of a dinner fork down the long way so that when cucumber is sliced it will have a fluted edge. Slice cucumber into ¼-inch slices. Slice eggs crosswise, forming round slices. Place a slice of egg on top of a slice of cucumber. Combine the chives, sour cream, sugar and Worcestershire sauce. Place a tiny dab of this mixture in the center of each egg slice, leaving yellow of egg still visible. Refrigerate until ready to serve.
Makes about 20 hors d'oeuvres. About 13 calories each.

SCALLOP BITES

1 pound scallops
1 teaspoon salt
1 teaspoon sugar
1 lemon, sliced
1 bay leaf

Rinse scallops thoroughly under cold running water. Cook about 5 minutes in boiling water, to which has been added salt, sugar, sliced lemon, and bay leaf. Drain; chill. Insert on wooden picks and serve as an hors d'oeuvre.
About 15 calories per scallop.

SHRIMP KABOBS

40 medium shrimp
1 green pepper, sliced in small cubes
6-8 mushrooms, sliced thick
1 can (6 ounce) frozen orange juice concentrate, thawed, undiluted
1 tablespoon soy sauce
2 tablespoons prepared mustard
1 tablespoon honey
1 small garlic clove, crushed
1 teaspoon powdered ginger

Shell and devein the shrimp; spear shrimp, green pepper, and mushrooms on skewers. Blend together undiluted orange concentrate, soy sauce, mustard, honey, garlic and ginger in a small saucepan. Brush kabobs with sauce. Place on hibachi or under broiler and grill for 10 minutes, turning once, and brush occasionally with sauce until shrimp is done.
About 18 calories per shrimp.

CHAPTER 5

SKINNY SOUPS

Cream soups are out, skinny soups are in! It's the only way you can afford to retain a soup course. These soups may be slender in calorie count, but they are designed to please your palate from first sip. Do remember that attractive bowls and interesting presentation add to the gratification of a soup course. Sometimes a mere sprinkling of minced parsley or a thin slice of lemon will give a clear soup the extra eye appeal you crave. It's the difference between feeding and dining!

ASPARAGUS BISQUE

1 cup asparagus spears, drained
½ cup liquid from asparagus
½ cup skim milk
1 teaspoon sugar
1 tablespoon sherry

Blend all ingredients together in a blender. Pour mixture into a saucepan and heat. Do not let mixture boil. Serve hot, with a dollop of sour cream if desired.
Serves 3. About 42 calories per serving, without sour cream.

CRABMEAT BISQUE

1 can condensed cream of tomato soup
1½ cans skim milk
1 can (6½ ounces) crabmeat
1 tablespoon chopped chives
2 teaspoons lemon juice
1 teaspoon sugar

Blend tomato soup and skim milk together in a saucepan until smooth. Add flaked crabmeat, chopped chives, lemon juice and sugar. Heat and serve in small cups.
Serves 6. About 87 calories per serving.

COLD FRUIT SOUP

2 tablespoons Minute Tapioca
1½ cups water
Dash of salt
1½ tablespoons lemon juice
1 package (10 ounces) sliced strawberries, thawed
1 cup diced orange sections

Cook and stir tapioca and water to a boil. Remove from heat. Add salt and lemon juice. Cool; stir often. Chill. Before serving, add strawberries and orange sections.
Serves 6. About 84 calories per serving.

SHRIMP GUMBO

½ onion, minced
½ green pepper, minced
2 stalks celery, minced
1 clove garlic, minced
1 package (10 ounces) frozen okra
1 can (1 pound) tomatoes
1½ cups water
2 bouillon cubes
½ teaspoon salt
½ teaspoon sugar
Dash pepper
Pinch thyme
Bay leaf
1 cup shrimp, cleaned, cut in half, lengthwise

Combine onion, green pepper, celery, garlic, okra and tomatoes in a saucepan. Add water and bouillon cubes. Simmer for a few minutes until bouillon cubes are melted. Add salt, sugar, pepper, thyme and bay leaf. Simmer for 15 minutes. Add cleaned, raw shrimp and simmer for an additional seven minutes, or until shrimp are tender.
Serves 6. About 49 calories per serving.

TOMATO-RICE SOUP

½ onion, minced
2 cups tomato juice
1½ cups water
2 bouillon cubes
½ teaspoon celery salt
¼ teaspoon salt
½ teaspoon sugar
Bay leaf
¼ cup cooked rice

Combine onion, tomato juice, water and bouillon cubes together in a saucepan. Simmer until bouillon cubes are melted. Add celery salt, salt, sugar, and bay leaf. Simmer, covered for 10 minutes. Add cooked rice and serve.
Serves 4. About 45 calories per serving.

GAZPACHO

1 can condensed tomato soup
2 tablespoons wine vinegar
1 clove garlic, minced
1 cup water
1 cucumber, chopped
½ onion, chopped
½ green pepper, chopped
½ teaspoon salt
1 teaspoon sugar
¼ teaspoon pepper
¼ teaspoon nutmeg

Thoroughly combine all ingredients—in a blender if you have one. Chill. Serve cold.
Serves 4. About 65 calories per serving.

CORN CHOWDER

½ cup clam juice
1 cup cream style corn
½ cup skim milk
1 tablespoon chopped onion
¼ teaspoon thyme
1 teaspoon sugar
½ cup minced clams

Combine clam juice and corn in a saucepan. Add skim milk, onion, thyme, sugar and minced clams. Heat all together, stirring occasionally. Let stand a while. Reheat to serve.
Serves 4. About 69 calories per serving.

TOMATO BOUILLON

2 cups tomato juice
1 cup bouillon
1 teaspoon lemon juice
½ teaspoon sugar
1 teaspoon parsley flakes

Simmer all together for 5 minutes, in a covered saucepan.
Serves 4. About 29 calories per serving.

JELLIED TOMATO SOUP WITH SHERRY

1 teaspoon unflavored gelatin
2 tablespoons cold water
1 cup tomato juice
¼ teaspoon monosodium glutamate
1 tablespoon sherry
1 teaspoon lemon juice

Mix gelatin with cold water in mixing bowl. Heat tomato juice, lemon juice and monosodium glutamate. Add sherry. Mix gelatin mixture into hot tomato mixture. Pour into soup cups and chill. Garnish with lemon wedge and parsley.
Serves 2. About 32 calories per serving.

VEGETABLE-CLAM BROTH

2 cups tomato-vegetable juice
½ cup clam juice
1 teaspoon lemon juice
½ teaspoon sugar

Simmer all together for 5 minutes.
Serves 4. About 32 calories per serving.

SPINACH SOUP

1 package frozen chopped spinach, thawed
2 cups chicken broth
1 tablespoon finely minced onion
½ teaspoon salt
⅛ teaspoon pepper
½ teaspoon sugar
Pinch of nutmeg

Empty thawed spinach and chicken broth into your blender. Add minced onion, salt, pepper, sugar and nutmeg. Blend. Pour into a saucepan and simmer for 20 minutes.
Serves 4. About 27 calories per serving.

BEEF EGG DROP SOUP

2 cans beef bouillon
½ teaspoon sugar
1 egg

Empty can of beef bouillon into a saucepan. Add sugar. Beat egg in a dish. Heat soup to boiling point and as it breaks into rapid swirls, stir in the beaten egg. Continue stirring as egg threads set. Serve immediately.
Serves 6. About 22 calories per serving.

SHERRY CONSOMME

2 cans (10½ ounces, each) chicken consomme
2 cups water
1 cup sherry
1 sliced lemon

Combine consomme and water. Heat, but do not boil; add sherry and heat 1 minute longer. Serve piping hot garnished with lemon slices.
Serves 8. About 63 calories per serving.

PUREE MONGOL SOUP

1 can condensed cream of tomato soup
1 soup can water
½ cup canned peas
½ teaspoon sugar
1 teaspoon lemon juice

Empty tomato soup, water and peas into a blender. Blend until smooth. Add sugar and lemon juice. Blend. Pour into a saucepan and heat.
Serves 4. About 77 calories per serving.

COCKALEEKIE SOUP

2 cups water
3 bouillon cubes
3 leeks, split and
　　cut in 1-inch pieces
½ teaspoon sugar
¼ teaspoon salt

⅛ teaspoon pepper
½ cup cooked chicken,
　　cut in strips
1 tablespoon minced parsley
¼ cup cooked rice

Simmer water and bouillon cubes together until cubes are melted. Add leeks, sugar, salt and pepper. Simmer until leeks are tender, about 15 minutes. Add chicken, parsley, and cooked rice. Simmer together for several minutes.
Serves 4. About 45 calories per serving.

JELLIED BEET BORSCH

1 package unflavored gelatin
1 can (1 pound) julienne
　　beets, drained, save liquid
1 can (10½ ounces)
　　consomme

½ cup onion, chopped
1 tablespoon sugar
2 tablespoons lemon juice

Sprinkle gelatin over beet liquid and stir well. Pour consomme into saucepan; add onions and simmer 10 minutes; strain. Add beets, sugar, lemon juice, and beet juice mixture to the consomme. Spoon into soup cups, or into a mold and chill. Serve cold with a dollop of sour cream, if desired.
Serves 4. About 69 calories per serving.

FRENCH ONION SOUP

2 cups thinly sliced onions
1 tablespoon butter
2 cups beef bouillon, canned
1 cup water
½ teaspoon salt
¼ teaspoon pepper
½ teaspoon sugar
1 tablespoon grated Parmesan cheese

Sauté onions in butter at the bottom of a saucepan. When onions are golden, add bouillon, water, salt, pepper and sugar. Simmer, covered for 20 minutes. Stir in cheese just before serving.
Serves 4. About 62 calories per serving.

ORIENTAL SPINACH SOUP

1 package (10 ounce) frozen spinach, whole leaf, cooked
2 cans (10½ ounce) condensed chicken broth
1 soup can water
1 tablespoon cornstarch
½ cup diced celery
2 tablespoons sliced green onion
2 teaspoons soy sauce

Drain cooked spinach and set aside. Combine chicken broth with water in a saucepan; stir in cornstarch, celery, green onion and soy sauce. Bring to a boil; simmer 5 minutes. Add cooked spinach. Serve in soup bowl. Garnish each bowl with additional sliced green onion, if desired.
Serves 8. About 33 calories per serving.

Oriental Spinach Soup (page 22)
Photo courtesy of the Green Giant Company

Flank Steak Burgundy (page 38)
Photo courtesy of Campbell Soup Company

CHAPTER 6

MELTING MAINSTAYS

Pounds can slip off as you enjoy the streamlined recipes for fish, chicken, veal and beef in this chapter. Portion-controlled for easy calorie counting, you will be able to judge just how many calories you are adding to your total intake. Old fashioned tastes have been retained, and new fashioned ideas about eating have been added, to give you a variety of gourmet main courses. Better not tell family or guests that these are diet dinners, they won't believe you!

CRABMEAT DIVAN

1 can (6½ ounces) king crabmeat
1 package frozen broccoli spears
1 can condensed cream of celery soup
1 tablespoon sherry
½ teaspoon prepared mustard
2 tablespoons grated Parmesan cheese

Drain crabmeat. Cook broccoli spears and drain. Arrange broccoli spears in a flat baking dish. Place pieces of crabmeat over broccoli. Combine undiluted soup with sherry and prepared mustard. Spread this mixture over the crabmeat. Sprinkle top with grated Parmesan cheese. Bake 20 minutes in a 350 degree oven.
Serves 4. About 128 calories per serving.

BROILED SCAMPI

1 pound large shrimp, peeled and cleaned, with tails on
2 tablespoons olive oil
1 clove crushed garlic
1 tablespoon minced parsley
½ teaspoon brown sugar
½ teaspoon salt
¼ teaspoon pepper

Split the shrimp into butterfly shape, leaving tails on. Combine oil, garlic, parsley, brown sugar, salt and pepper. Arrange shrimp on a broiling pan, brush with oil mixture, broil for 3 minutes on each side. Serve with wedges of lemon.
Serves 4. About 154 calories per portion.

BAKED STUFFED SHRIMP

12 jumbo shrimp
¼ pound scallops
1 tablespoon butter, melted
¼ teaspoon paprika
½ teaspoon brown sugar

2 tablespoons crushed potato chips
2 tablespoons grated Parmesan cheese
1 tablespoon sherry (optional)

Cut shrimp through the shell from the underside, being careful not to cut entirely in half. Remove veins and spread flat into butterfly shape. Arrange shrimp on a baking pan. Chop scallops. Spoon in center of shrimp. Combine melted butter, paprika, brown sugar, crushed potato chips and grated Parmesan cheese. Spoon over scallops and spread over rest of exposed shrimp. Bake in a 350 degree oven for 20 minutes, sprinkling with sherry during the last 5 minutes of baking.
Serves 4. About 146 calories per serving.

SHRIMP SAUTÉ

20 large shrimp, peeled and cleaned
1 cup chicken broth
1 cup white wine
1 bay leaf

1 tablespoon minced parsley
½ teaspoon sugar
½ teaspoon salt
1 tablespoon lemon juice

Place shrimp, butterflied (cut partially through lengthwise and flattened), in a single layer in a large skillet. Add broth and wine. Add bay leaf, parsley, sugar, salt, and lemon juice. Bring to a boil, then simmer for 5 minutes, stirring occasionally. Serve at once.
Serves 4. About 107 calories per serving.

SHRIMP STEW

1 pound raw shrimp,
  shelled and cleaned
¼ cup lemon juice
1 sweet onion, sliced thin
2 tomatoes, cut up
1 clove garlic, crushed

1 tablespoon dried
  parsley flakes
1 teaspoon sugar
½ teaspoon salt
¼ teaspoon pepper
½ teaspoon thyme
2 tablespoons butter

Combine shrimp, lemon juice, and onion in a bowl. Add cut up tomatoes, garlic, parsley flakes, sugar, salt, pepper and thyme. Stir and refrigerate until ready to cook (can marinate like this for several hours). To cook, melt butter in a skillet and empty the bowl into it. Cover and cook for 8 to 10 minutes, or until shrimp are pink. Delicious spooned over rice.
Serves 4. About 170 calories per serving.

SHRIMP NEWBURG

1 pound shrimp,
  cleaned and cooked
1 can condensed
  cream of celery soup

½ cup skim milk
1 tablespoon sherry
2 tablespoons grated
  Parmesan cheese

Combine undiluted celery soup, skim milk, sherry and Parmesan cheese in a saucepan. Simmer until cheese is melted and add shrimp; simmer for several minutes more. Serve at once.
Serves 4. About 142 calories per serving.

BROILED SWORDFISH WITH BARBECUE SAUCE

6 swordfish steaks, totalling 2 pounds
1 teaspoon salt
½ teaspoon pepper
¼ cup onion, chopped fine
¼ cup green pepper, chopped fine

¼ cup chili sauce
2 tablespoons ketchup
2 tablespoons lemon juice
1 tablespoon brown sugar
½ teaspoon mustard
1 teaspoon Worcestershire sauce

Arrange swordfish steaks on a broiling pan, season with salt and pepper, and broil for 5-6 minutes on each side. Meanwhile, in a small saucepan, combine remaining ingredients. Simmer, covered, until fish is done. Then spoon mixture over each steak and serve at once.
Serves 6. About 127 calories per serving.

POACHED SALMON

2-pound slice, center cut, fresh salmon
1 quart water
½ cup cider vinegar
1 onion, sliced
3 cloves

Several sprigs of dill or 1 tablespoon dried dill
1 bay leaf
1 teaspoon salt
1 teaspoon sugar

Put water, vinegar and onion in a large saucepan. Add onion, cloves, dill, bay leaf, salt and sugar. Bring to a boil. Add salmon and simmer for 15-20 minutes, or until salmon is flaky but still whole. Remove salmon from water and serve hot or chilled.
Serves 6. About 278 calories per serving.

FLOUNDER FLORENTINE

1 pound fillets of flounder, sliced thin
1 package frozen chopped spinach, thawed
1 tablespoon butter
¼ cup lemon juice
½ teaspoon sugar
¼ teaspoon salt

Fold fillets in half, lengthwise. Roll up—fasten with toothpicks if necessary—and place around edge of a baking dish. Fill center carefully with spinach. In a small saucepan, combine butter, lemon juice, sugar and salt. Heat until butter is melted. Spoon over tops of fish rolls. Bake uncovered at 350 degrees for about 25 minutes, or until fish flakes easily but is still moist. Serves 4. About 132 calories per serving.

BANANA SOLE AMANDINE

1 pound fillet of sole, 4 slices
1 large banana
2 tablespoons lemon juice
½ teaspoon sugar
1 tablespoon almonds, chopped

Arrange fillets on a broiling pan. Cut banana in half lengthwise, then crosswise. Mix lemon juice and sugar together. Roll banana in the mixture and place one piece of banana in the center of each fillet. Broil for 15-20 minutes, or until done. Sprinkle with chopped almonds.
Serves 4. About 129 calories per serving.

BROILED FILLET OF SOLE WITH CHEESE SAUCE

1 pound fillets of sole
¼ cup lemon juice
½ teaspoon sugar
½ teaspoon salt
¼ teaspoon pepper

¼ cup sour cream
2 tablespoons grated
  cheddar cheese
1 teaspoon paprika

Arrange fillets on a flat broiling pan. Stir sugar into lemon juice and pour over fish. Sprinkle fish with salt and pepper. Spread each fillet with a thin coating of sour cream. Sprinkle cheddar cheese over the sour cream, and top with a dash of paprika. Broil 10-15 minutes, or until fish is flaky but firm. Serves 4. About 132 calories per serving.

CUCUMBER-CREAM BROILED FILLETS

1 pound fillet of flounder,
  4 slices
¼ cup sour cream
½ cucumber, peeled
¼ teaspoon salt

¼ teaspoon
  Worcestershire sauce
1 teaspoon lemon juice
½ teaspoon sugar
½ teaspoon paprika

Arrange fillets in a flat broiling pan. In a blender, combine sour cream, cut up cucumber, salt, Worcestershire sauce, lemon juice and sugar. Blend until smooth. Spread on fish and sprinkle with paprika. Broil 15 minutes, or until done. Serve at once, garnished with thinly sliced cucumber.
Serves 4. About 114 calories per serving.

BROILED FISH PARMESAN

1 pound fillets of flounder
½ teaspoon salt
¼ teaspoon pepper
1 tablespoon grated onion
1 tomato, chopped
1 teaspoon brown sugar
1 tablespoon grated
 Parmesan cheese

Arrange fillets in a flat broiling pan. Sprinkle with salt and pepper. Combine grated onion, chopped tomato and brown sugar; place a thin layer on top of each fillet. Top with grated Parmesan cheese. Broil for 10-15 minutes.
Serves 4. About 108 calories per serving.

BRUNSWICK STEW

1 chicken, cut up
 (about 3 pounds)
1½ cups water
1 onion, sliced thin
1 can tomatoes (1 pound)
1 teaspoon salt
¼ teaspoon pepper
2 potatoes, peeled and
 cut in chunks
1 can whole corn, drained
1 can okra, drained
1 teaspoon brown sugar
1 teaspoon
 Worcestershire sauce
¼ cup sherry (optional)

Place chicken parts in a deep saucepan. Add water, onion, tomatoes, salt and pepper. Simmer, covered, for 15 minutes. Add chunks of potatoes, corn, okra, sugar and Worcestershire sauce. Simmer, covered for 15 minutes more. Add sherry, cover and simmer until chicken and potatoes are tender.
Serves 4. About 355 calories per serving.

CHICKEN LIVER KABOBS

1 pound chicken livers
2 green peppers
½ pound mushrooms
1 tablespoon salad oil

1 teaspoon brown sugar
1 teaspoon soy sauce
½ teaspoon salt
¼ teaspoon pepper

Cut livers in half. Cut peppers in small squares, removing seeds and membranes. Remove stems from mushrooms and reserve for use another time. Combine salad oil, brown sugar, soy sauce, salt and pepper. Using 8 skewers, alternate pieces of chicken liver, peppers, and mushrooms. Brush with sauce and broil for 8 minutes, turning once.
Serves 4. About 216 calories per serving.

CHICKEN LIVERS MANDARIN

½ pound chicken livers
1 thinly sliced onion
1 can (6 ounces) mandarin oranges
1 can (4 ounces) sliced mushrooms

½ cup water
1 teaspoon cornstarch
1 teaspoon lemon juice
1 teaspoon brown sugar
½ teaspoon salt
1 teaspoon soy sauce

Drain juice of oranges and mushrooms into a skillet. Add quartered chicken livers and onion slices. Cover and simmer for 10 minutes. Add orange slices and mushrooms. In a cup, combine water, cornstarch, lemon juice, brown sugar, salt and soy sauce. Blend smoothly; pour into skillet and stir all ingredients together. Heat until sauce thickens slightly. Serve immediately.
Serves 2. About 238 calories per serving.

OVEN-FRIED CHICKEN PARMESAN

1 fryer, cut up
½ cup skim milk
1 cup herb stuffing, crushed
2 tablespoons Parmesan cheese, grated

Dip pieces of chicken in milk, coating well. Combine crushed herb stuffing with Parmesan cheese. Bread chicken parts with this mixture. Arrange chicken in a baking pan. Bake at 375 degrees for 45 minutes.
Serves 4. About 251 calories per serving.

BARBECUED BROILED CHICKEN

1 broiling chicken
 (about 3 pounds), quartered
1 tablespoon butter
1 teaspoon paprika
1 teaspoon brown sugar
2 tablespoons vinegar
½ teaspoon salt
¼ teaspoon pepper
1 teaspoon Worcestershire sauce

Arrange chicken, skin side down, on a broiling rack. Combine remaining ingredients in a saucepan and simmer until butter is melted and ingredients are blended. Brush chicken with half the mixture. Broil for 15-20 minutes. Turn and brush chicken with remaining sauce. Broil until chicken is tender.
Serves 4. About 228 calories per serving.

BAKED CHICKEN IN FOIL

1 broiling chicken, quartered
2 tablespoons wine vinegar
2 tablespoons lemon juice
1 tablespoon brown sugar

½ teaspoon salt
¼ teaspoon mustard
⅛ teaspoon pepper

Arrange each quarter of chicken on a square of foil. Combine remaining ingredients and brush liberally on all sides of chicken. Wrap airtight in foil. Bake for 1 hour at 350 degrees, or place on outdoor grill, turning every 15 minutes.
Serves 4. About 212 calories per serving.

POTTED CHICKEN WITH ARTICHOKE

3-pound chicken
1 can whole tomatoes
1 onion, sliced
1 green pepper, cut up
1 can artichoke hearts

1 tablespoon lemon juice
1 teaspoon sugar
½ teaspoon salt
2 teaspoons paprika
½ cup white wine (optional)

Place cleaned chicken in a Dutch oven or heavy pot. Add tomatoes, including juice. Add onion, green pepper and artichoke hearts, including juice. Add lemon juice, sugar and salt. Sprinkle paprika over chicken. Cover tightly and simmer for 30 minutes. Add white wine and simmer for an additional 15 minutes, or until tender.
Serves 4. About 242 calories per portion.

ORIENTAL CHICKEN KABOBS

6 boneless chicken breasts
1 can (13½ ounces) pineapple chunks
¼ cup soy sauce
1 tablespoon cornstarch
1 teaspoon brown sugar
¼ teaspoon ginger
12 medium mushrooms
2 green peppers, cut in 1-inch squares

Cut chicken meat into large chunks for kabobs. Drain juice from pineapple into a saucepan. Add soy sauce, cornstarch, brown sugar and ginger. Heat and stir until mixture is thickened. Arrange chicken, mushrooms, and green pepper alternately on skewers. Place these in a small flat pan. Brush sauce over kabobs, coating well. Bake in a 350 degree oven for 25 minutes. Serves 6. About 261 calories per portion.

CHICKEN LUAU

6 boneless chicken breasts
½ teaspoon salt
1 tablespoon cornstarch
1 can (13½ ounces) pineapple chunks
1 teaspoon brown sugar
¼ teaspoon ground ginger

Arrange chicken breasts in a small roasting pan. Sprinkle with salt. Put a tablespoon of cornstarch into a small bowl, drain pineapple juice into it and blend until smooth. Add pineapple chunks, brown sugar, and ground ginger. Pour over chicken breasts, coating them well. Bake in a 350 degree oven for 25 minutes, basting occasionally with sauce in the pan. Serves 6. About 235 calories per serving.

CHICKEN ROSEMARY

1 chicken, about 3 pounds
1 can whole tomatoes
1 green pepper
1 tablespoon rosemary

1 teaspoon salt
1 teaspoon sugar
¼ teaspoon pepper
½ cup white wine (optional)

Place chicken in a Dutch oven. Add tomatoes and diced green pepper. Add rosemary, salt, sugar and pepper. Simmer, covered for 30 minutes. Add white wine. Simmer another 15 minutes, or until tender.
Serves 4. About 232 calories per serving.

ORANGE NUGGET ROAST TURKEY

1 turkey (8 to 12 pounds)
5 oranges, unpeeled
3 slices day old bread, torn in small pieces

1 tablespoon brown sugar
¼ teaspoon salt
⅛ teaspoon pepper

Rinse turkey, drain and pat dry with paper towels. Cut 3 oranges into chunks; combine with bread pieces, brown sugar, salt and pepper. Spoon orange chunk mixture into turkey, and close with skewers. Place turkey, breast side up, on rack in shallow roasting pan. Cover breast bone area only with a large strip of aluminum foil. Roast at 325 degrees for 3 to 4 hours, depending on the size of the turkey. While turkey is roasting, squeeze juice form remaining oranges, and use for basting turkey during roasting. When done, remove orange stuffing and discard. Let turkey rest for 20 minutes for easier carving.
Serves 8-10. About 160 calories per 2-slice serving.

HERB-BAKED TURKEY ROLL

1 rolled turkey roast (about 4 pounds)
2 tablespoons melted butter
2 tablespoons chopped parsley
½ teaspoon salt
½ teaspoon marjoram
½ teaspoon paprika
¼ teaspoon pepper
2 tablespoons sherry

Arrange turkey roast in a small baking pan. Combine melted butter and seasonings in a small saucepan. Add sherry and simmer for several minutes. Brush turkey roll with this mixture. Cover top of roll with a loose piece of aluminum foil. Bake in a 325 oven for 1½ hours, or until tender. Remove foil the last 15 minutes of roasting if a browner crust is desired.
Serves 8-10. About 329 calories per ¼ pound portion.

STEAK MARINADE

2-pound boneless round steak, trimmed lean
Meat tenderizer
1 cup red wine
1 clove garlic, minced
½ teaspoon sugar
½ teaspoon salt
¼ teaspoon pepper
1 teaspoon Worcestershire sauce

Apply meat tenderizer on all surfaces of steak. Let stand the directed time. Combine wine, garlic, sugar, salt, pepper and Worcestershire sauce. Marinate meat in sauce for 2 hours in the refrigerator, turning occasionally. Remove steak from marinade and broil for 8-10 minutes on each side, until desired degree of rareness is achieved. Slice on a slight angle as for London Broil.
Serves 8. About 225 calories per serving.

SWISS STEAK

2-pound slice of top
  round steak
2 tablespoons flour
½ teaspoon salt
¼ teaspoon pepper

1 slice bacon
1 onion, sliced
2 teaspoons brown sugar
1 cup grapefruit juice

Combine flour, salt, and pepper. Pound into surface of steak on all sides. In a Dutch oven, cook the slice of bacon until most of the fat is melted. Brown steak in the bacon fat on all sides. Remove, brown onions in remaining fat, until golden. Add brown sugar to grapefruit juice. Return steak to pan, pour juice around steak, cover and cook for 1 hour, or until tender.
Serves 6. About 333 calories per serving.

FLANK STEAK TERIYAKI

1 flank steak, about 2 pounds
¼ cup soy sauce
1 tablespoon brown sugar

½ teaspoon ginger
1 clove crushed garlic
1 teaspoon salad oil

Place flank steak on a broiling rack. Combine soy sauce, sugar, ginger, garlic, and oil. Brush half on top of steak. Broil 10 minutes. Turn and brush remaining sauce on top of steak. Broil 5 to 10 minutes more, depending on desired degree of rareness. Slice steak on a wide angle as for London Broil.
Serves 4. About 365 calories per serving.

FLANK STEAK BURGUNDY

1 can (10½ ounces)
   condensed onion soup
2 tablespoons Burgundy wine
½ teaspoon basil, crushed
1½ pounds flank steak, scored

Combine condensed onion soup, Burgundy, and crushed basil; pour over flank steak in a shallow dish. Refrigerate for 1 hour; turn meat occasionally. Place on grill about 4 inches above glowing coals, or place in broiling pan. Cook 5 minutes on each side or until desired doneness; brush frequently with marinade. Heat remaining sauce; serve with meat thinly sliced diagonally across grain.
Serves 6. About 178 calories per serving.

SWEET STEAK

2-pound flank steak
½ teaspoon salt
¼ teaspoon pepper
1 tablespoon mustard
2 tablespoons brown sugar

Salt and pepper steak. Spread mustard lightly on both sides. Place on broiling rack. Sprinkle 1 tablespoon of brown sugar on top. Broil for 4 minutes. Turn. Sprinkle the remaining tablespoon of brown sugar on top. Broil 4 minutes more, or until degree of desired rareness is reached. Slice on the diagonal as for London Broil.
Serves 4. About 349 calories per serving.

STUFFED FLANK STEAK

1 flank steak, about 1 pound
1 onion, diced
1 package frozen chopped spinach (thawed)
½ teaspoon salt
¼ teaspoon pepper
¼ teaspoon nutmeg
1 slice toast

1 cup canned tomatoes with juice
1 onion, sliced thin
1 green pepper, minced
½ cup water
½ teaspoon sugar
½ teaspoon salt

Combine diced onion, thawed spinach, salt, pepper and nutmeg. Crumble toast and add to spinach mixture. Spread mixture over top of flank steak and roll up, jelly-roll fashion. In a Dutch oven, put tomatoes and juice. Add sliced onion, green pepper, water, sugar and salt. Simmer for 10 minutes, stirring. Place rolled flank steak in this sauce, cover and simmer for 1 hour.
Serves 4. About 238 calories per serving.

ZESTY MEAT LOAF

2 pounds lean ground round beef
1 egg, beaten
1 tablespoon ketchup
1 teaspoon soy sauce

1 teaspoon brown sugar
½ teaspoon salt
¼ teaspoon pepper
1 small onion, grated

Mix ground beef, egg, ketchup and soy sauce together. Add brown sugar, salt, pepper, and grated onion. Fill a loaf pan with the mixture and bake at 350 degrees for 1 hour.
Serves 6. About 319 calories per serving.

MEATBALL STEW

1 pound lean ground beef
1 tablespoon grated
  Parmesan cheese
½ teaspoon salt
¼ teaspoon pepper
1 tablespoon chopped
  dried parsley
1 can whole tomatoes
  (1 pound)
1 clove garlic, minced

1 sliced onion
1 green pepper, cut up
2 carrots, cut in chunks
4 stalks celery, cut in chunks
2 potatoes, peeled
  and quartered
1 package frozen,
  cut up green beans
1 bay leaf
1 teaspoon sugar

Combine ground beef, Parmesan cheese, salt, pepper and parsley. Add water if necessary to soften mixture. Empty can of tomatoes into a large saucepan. Add minced garlic and sliced onion. Add green pepper, carrots, celery and potatoes. Add bay leaf and sugar. Form meat mixture into tiny balls. Place in pot on top of vegetables. Cover and simmer for 30 minutes. Add frozen green beans. Simmer for 10 minutes more.
Serves 4. About 368 calories per serving.

HERBED BURGERS

1 pound lean ground beef
½ teaspoon salt
¼ teaspoon pepper
¼ teaspoon marjoram

¼ teaspoon thyme
½ onion, grated
2 tablespoons lemon juice
1 teaspoon soy sauce

Combine all ingredients, adding water if necessary to make mixture lighter. Form into 4 large patties. Broil about 10 minutes, depending on degree of rareness desired. Serve at once.
Serves 4. About 232 calories per serving.

SAVORY MEAT LOAF

2 pounds lean ground beef
⅓ cup Minute Tapioca
⅓ cup finely chopped onion
1½ teaspoon salt
½ teaspoon sugar
¼ teaspoon pepper
1½ cups canned tomatoes, mashed

Combine ingredients, mixing well. Pack lightly in a 10 x 5 x 3-inch loaf pan. Bake 1 hour at 350 degrees.
Serves 8. About 283 calories per serving.

BOILED BEEF WITH DILL SAUCE

3-pound piece of top round roast
1 onion, sliced
2 cups boiling water
2 bay leaves
½ teaspoon salt
¼ teaspoon pepper

Place beef in a Dutch oven or heavy saucepan, add sliced onion. Pour boiling water over beef. Add bay leaves, salt and pepper. Cover and simmer for about 3 hours, or until tender. Slice and serve with Dill Sauce.

DILL SAUCE:

1 tablespoon butter
1 tablespoon cornstarch
1 cup gravy from boiled beef
1 tablespoon chopped dill
1 tablespoon lemon juice
1 teaspoon sugar
¼ teaspoon salt

Melt butter in a small saucepan and stir in cornstarch. Add gravy, stirring constantly. Add chopped dill, lemon juice, sugar and salt. Stir until mixture is thickened. Serve over boiled beef.
Serves 8. About 361 calories per serving.

STEAK DIANE

2-pound sirloin steak
  (boneless), well trimmed
½ teaspoon salt
¼ teaspoon pepper
2 tablespoons lemon juice

1 tablespoon butter
½ teaspoon brown sugar
½ teaspoon Worcestershire
  sauce
1 tablespoon chopped chives

Salt and pepper the steak, and broil on both sides until desired degree of rareness is achieved. Meanwhile, combine lemon juice, butter, brown sugar, Worcestershire sauce, and chives in a small saucepan. Stir and heat through. Pour over steak just before serving.
Serves 6. About 436 calories per serving.

BEEF ROULADES

8 thin sliced beef roulades
  (about 2 pounds)
½ teaspoon salt
¼ teaspoon pepper
½ teaspoon monosodium
  glutamate
2 tablespoons minced parsley

1 can (3 ounces) deviled ham
1 cup dry red wine
1 tablespoon tomato paste
½ teaspoon sugar
½ teaspoon dillweed
  (optional)

Sprinkle slices of beef with salt, pepper, and monosodium glutamate. Combine parsley and deviled ham. Spread thinly over one side of each slice of beef. Starting at one end, roll up each slice jelly-roll fashion. Place in a shallow casserole, close to each other. Combine wine, tomato paste, sugar, and dillweed; pour over roulades. Cover tightly and bake in a 35 degree oven for 45 minutes.
Serves 4. About 390 calories per serving.

SAVORY MINUTE STEAKS

8 minute steaks, ¼ pound each
2 tablespoons olive oil
1 onion, sliced paper thin
1 clove garlic, minced
1 can (8 ounces) tomato sauce
½ cup water
1 teaspoon oregano
½ teaspoon basil
½ teaspoon salt
¼ teaspoon pepper
½ teaspoon sugar

Brown steaks quickly in oil, using a heavy skillet. Add onion and garlic; sauté for several minutes. Add tomato sauce, water, oregano, basil, salt, pepper and sugar. Stir sauce and spoon over minute steaks. Cover and simmer for 20 minutes, basting occasionally. Serve at once.
Serves 8. About 363 calories per serving.

SWEET AND SOUR LAMB CHOPS

6 large loin lamb chops, lean and well trimmed of fat
1 teaspoon salt
1 teaspoon paprika
1 teaspoon brown sugar
⅛ teaspoon pepper
1 cup orange juice
¼ teaspoon cinnamon

Broil lamb chops for 5 minutes on each side. Remove from broiler and place in large skillet. Combine salt, paprika, brown sugar, pepper, orange juice and cinnamon. Pour over chops; cover and simmer for 20 minutes, or until tender.
Serves 6. About 207 calories per chop.

BROILED LAMB CHOPS, ITALIENNE

8 shoulder lamb chops, about 2 pounds
¼ cup wine vinegar
2 tablespoons lemon juice
1 tablespoon olive oil
1 clove garlic, crushed
1 teaspoon sugar
¾ teaspoon oregano
1 teaspoon salt
¼ teaspoon pepper

Arrange lamb chops on a rack in a broiling pan. Combine remaining ingredients in a tightly closed jar and shake vigorously. Brush mixture on lamb chops and broil for 8 minutes on one side. Turn and brush remaining mixture on other side. Broil until done, about 6 minutes more.
Serves 8. About 345 calories per serving.

CURRIED LAMB STEW

1½ pounds boneless lamb, cubed
1 onion, diced
4 celery stalks, diced
1 clove garlic, minced
½ pound fresh mushrooms, sliced
2 tablespoons tomato paste
1 cup water
2 teaspoons curry powder
1 teaspoon brown sugar
½ teaspoon salt
¼ teaspoon pepper

Trim lamb to remove fat. In a large skillet, place diced onion, celery, minced garlic, mushrooms, tomato paste and water. Stir. Simmer, covered for 10 minutes. Add curry powder, brown sugar, salt and pepper. Add cubes of lamb. Cover and simmer for about 1 hour, or until meat is tender.
Serves 6. About 284 calories per serving.

LEG OF LAMB JARDINIERE

4-pound leg of lamb
2 teaspoons salt
1 teaspoon brown sugar
1 clove garlic, crushed
1 teaspoon rosemary

½ teaspoon paprika
3 large potatoes, quartered
2 onions, sliced
4 carrots

Place leg of lamb in a roasting pan. Combine salt, brown sugar, garlic, rosemary and paprika. Rub mixture all over leg of lamb. Pour 1 cup of water around the roast and bake uncovered in a 400 degree oven for 30 minutes. Meanwhile, parboil peeled potatoes in boiling salted water. Drain and add to lamb, along with onions and carrots. Add additional water if necessary. Cover and bake for 40 minutes to an hour longer, or until tender. Serves 8. About 367 calories per serving, ¼ pound each.

LAMB SHANKS À L'ORANGE

8 lamb shanks
Meat tenderizer
1 can (6 ounces) undiluted frozen orange juice

1 tablespoon parsley
1 teaspoon brown sugar
1 tablespoon butter
½ teaspoon salt

Sprinkle lamb shanks with meat tenderizer as per directions on label. In a small saucepan, empty orange juice concentrate. Add parsley, brown sugar, butter and salt. Heat and stir until butter is melted. Arrange shanks in a roasting pan. Brush sauce over surfaces. Roast 1 hour, basting occasionally with remaining sauce. Reheat remaining sauce and pour over lamb shanks when ready to serve.
Serves 8. About 282 calories per serving.

LEG OF LAMB AU CAFÉ

1 leg of lamb
½ teaspoon salt
¼ teaspoon pepper
½ teaspoon garlic salt

1 teaspoon paprika
1 cup strong black coffee
1 teaspoon sugar

Season leg of lamb with salt, pepper, garlic salt and paprika. Place in a roasting pan. Stir sugar into black coffee (can be made with instant coffee, double strength) and pour over roast. Roast in a 400 degree oven for 2½ hours, basting occasionally. Allow about ¼-pound of sliced lamb per portion.
About 235 calories per serving.

VEAL STROGONOFF

2-pound boned
  shoulder of veal roast
1 onion, sliced
2 cloves
1 clove garlic, minced
1 bay leaf

2 tablespoons chopped dill
1 teaspoon salt
½ teaspoon sugar
1 tablespoon lemon juice
2 cups water
2 tablespoons sour cream

Place veal roast in a Dutch oven. Add onion, cloves, garlic, bay leaf and chopped dill around the roast. Sprinkle all with salt, sugar and lemon juice. Add water around the roast. Cover tightly and bake in a 350 degree oven for about 1½ hours, or until tender. Remove roast, remove bay leaf and simmer remaining gravy on the top of the stove, to reduce volume. Just before serving, stir in sour cream. Simmer but do not let the mixture boil. Serve over veal. Serves 6. About 251 calories per serving.

VEAL SAUTÉ

1 pound veal scallopini
¼ cup lemon juice
½ teaspoon sugar
1 egg
½ teaspoon mustard

⅓ cup fine bread crumbs
¼ teaspoon salt
Dash of pepper
2 tablespoons butter

Flatten veal steaks. Arrange in a flat casserole and pour lemon juice and sugar mixture over steaks. Turn often for several hours, until all of juice is absorbed. Beat egg, add mustard, and dip slices first in the egg batter and then in the combined bread crumbs, salt and pepper. Heat butter in a skillet. Brown veal on both sides, cover and simmer for several minutes. Serve at once. Serves 4. About 392 calories per serving.

VEAL SCALLOPINI

1 pound veal slices
¼ cup flour
2 tablespoons butter
1 cup tomato juice
1 tablespoon lemon juice

1 teaspoon sugar
1 teaspoon oregano
½ teaspoon salt
¼ teaspoon pepper
¼ teaspoon garlic powder

Lightly flour veal slices. Melt butter in a skillet and brown the floured veal slices. In a small saucepan, combine the tomato juice, lemon juice, sugar, oregano, salt, pepper and garlic powder. Heat and stir for several minutes. Pour over the veal, cover skillet and simmer for about 15 minutes.
Serves 4. About 289 calories per serving.

SAVORY VEAL ROAST

2-pound boned, rolled
  shoulder of veal roast
1 onion, sliced thin
1 clove garlic, minced
½ teaspoon salt
½ teaspoon pepper
1 teaspoon brown sugar
2 teaspoons paprika
1 can beef bouillon
2 scraped carrots

In a Dutch oven, arrange veal and onion. Add garlic, salt, pepper, brown sugar and paprika. Pour bouillon around roast and add the carrots. Cover and simmer for 2 hours, or until tender. Put gravy through a food mill or a blender. Pour over veal slices.
Serves 6. About 251 calories per serving.

BARBECUED SPARERIBS

2 pounds lean spareribs
¼ cup brown sugar
1 teaspoon mustard
1 teaspoon salt
¼ teaspoon black pepper
½ teaspoon ginger
¼ teaspoon cinnamon
½ cup tomato sauce
⅓ cup cider vinegar
½ teaspoon Tabasco sauce
1 tablespoon grated onion
1 clove garlic, crushed

Place spareribs on a rack in a large shallow pan. Roast in a 350 degree oven for 30 minutes. Pour off excess fat.
Blend sugar and spices. Add remaining ingredients. Bring to a boil, stirring constantly. Paint the ribs on both sides with about one-third of the sauce. Roast for 30 minutes more. Turn ribs, paint with about another third of the sauce and continue roasting and basting with remaining sauce until ribs are tender. Serves 4. About 486 calories per serving.

CHAPTER 7

VAIN VEGETABLES

Vegetables are good low-calorie, vitamin rich, high-satisfaction additions to your meal. Choose several to go with each main course and you will never miss the elimination of heavy starchy accompaniments you have eaten in the past. Properly prepared vegetables can present color and glamour to your dining. Here is a parade of savory concoctions created for discriminating dieters.

ASPARAGUS AU GRATIN

1 can (1 pound) green asparagus spears
2 tablespoons fine breadcrumbs
2 tablespoons grated Parmesan cheese

Arrange asparagus spears side by side in a small flat baking dish. Sprinkle evenly with bread crumbs and Parmesan cheese. Slip under the broiler for a few minutes, until cheese is melted. Serve at once.
Serves 4. About 36 calories per serving.

ASPARAGUS VINAIGRETTE

1 can asparagus spears (1 pound)
¼ cup white vinegar
¾ cup water
½ cup chopped mint
⅛ cup lemon juice
1 teaspoon sugar
2 tablespoons chopped onion

Place asparagus spears into a serving bowl. In a saucepan, heat together the vinegar, water, mint, lemon juice, sugar and chopped onion. Pour over asparagus. Serve hot or cold.
Serves 4. About 32 calories per serving.

ZIPPY GREEN BEANS

1 can cut green beans
2 tablespoons vinegar
¼ teaspoon salt
¼ teaspoon paprika
¼ teaspoon mustard
½ teaspoon sugar
Dash of pepper

Empty green beans into a saucepan, with half the amount of juice. Add remaining ingredients. Stir to blend. Heat through and serve hot or chilled.
Serves 4. About 16 calories per serving.

GREEN BEANS POLYNESIAN

1 large ripe pineapple
¼ cup chopped onion
2 tablespoons butter
¼ cup sugar
¼ cup vinegar
1 tablespoon soy sauce
1 teaspoon dry mustard
1 tablespoon cornstarch
1 can (5 ounces) water chestnuts, drained and sliced
2 cans (1 pound each) diagonal-cut green beans, drained

Cut pineapple in half, keeping leaves intact and cutting through them. Loosen and remove pineapple fruit, being careful not to puncture shell. Core and dice 1½ cups pineapple. Drain off ¼ cup pineapple juice. Reserve remaining pineapple and juice for other use. Sauté onion in butter until tender. Stir in sugar, vinegar, soy sauce and mustard. Combine cornstarch with pineapple juice; stir into onion mixture. Bring to a boil, stirring constantly. Add diced pineapple, water chestnuts and beans; reheat. Heat pineapple halves in 350 degree oven for 10 minutes. Serve beans in pineapple halves.
Serves 8. About 105 calories per serving.

MARINATED BEANS

1 can whole green beans, drained (16 ounces)
¼ cup wine vinegar
1 teaspoon salt
1 tablespoon sugar
½ teaspoon dillweed
Strips of pimiento

Place green beans in shallow refrigerator dish. Combine vinegar, salt, sugar and dillweed together. Pour over the green beans, cover tightly and refrigerate. Shake container occasionally to distribute the marinade. Serve cold with strips of pimiento. Serves 4. About 34 calories per serving.

GREEN BEANS AND TOMATOES

1 can green beans (1 pound)
1 cup canned peeled tomatoes
1 tablespoon chopped onion
½ teaspoon brown sugar
½ teaspoon grated Parmesan cheese
1 teaspoon lemon juice
½ teaspoon oregano

Drain juice of beans and tomatoes into a saucepan. Add chopped onion, cheese, sugar, lemon juice and oregano. Heat and stir until well blended. Add beans and tomatoes. Serve hot. Serves 4. About 38 calories per serving.

GREEN BEANS PARMESAN

1 can (16 ounces) green beans, French-cut
½ teaspoon sugar
½ teaspoon dried dillweed
2 tablespoons grated Parmesan cheese

Drain juice from can of beans into a saucepan. Add sugar and dried dillweed. Simmer and reduce volume by half. Add beans and heat through. Drain juice off, and add Parmesan cheese, mixing well. Serve at once.
Serves 4. About 33 calories per serving.

ISLAND GREEN BEANS

1 can (16 ounces) cut green beans, drained
1 can (8¾ ounces) pineapple tidbits, water-packed
1 tablespoon grated onion
1 tablespoon brown sugar
1 teaspoon soy sauce
¼ teaspoon dry mustard
1 teaspoon cornstarch

Empty cut green beans into a saucepan. Add pineapple tidbits with juice. Add grated onion, brown sugar, soy sauce and dry mustard. Blend cornstarch with a little water until smooth. Add cornstarch mixture to the saucepan. Heat, stirring, until beans and pineapple are well coated with sauce and the sauce has reached a bubbling thickened stage. Serve hot.
Serves 4. About 57 calories per serving.

DILLY BRUSSELS SPROUTS

1 package (10 ounce) Brussels sprouts frozen in butter sauce in cooking pouch

2 tablespoons dairy sour cream
1 teaspoon dill seed
½ teaspoon honey

Cook package of Brussels sprouts according to directions on label. Open; ease contents into serving dish. Lightly stir in sour cream, dill seed and honey. Serve at once.
Serves 3. About 103 calories per serving.

BROCCOLI CHIFFON

1 package (10 ounce) broccoli spears frozen in butter sauce in cooking pouch.

1 egg, separated
1½ teaspoons prepared mustard
½ teaspoon brown sugar

Drop frozen pouch of broccoli spears in butter sauce into boiling water to cover. Bring to a second boil. Cook 16 minutes, turning several times to insure complete cooking. While broccoli is cooking, blend egg yolk, mustard, and sugar. Beat egg white until stiff peaks form. Remove broccoli package from water, partially open and drain butter sauce into a small saucepan. Briskly stir in mustard-egg yolk mixture. Cook over low heat, stirring constantly until slightly thickened. Fold in beaten egg white. Spoon sauce over hot broccoli.
Serves 3. About 105 calories per serving.

BRUSSELS SPROUTS

1 package (10 ounces) frozen Brussels sprouts
1 cup water
1 teaspoon salt
½ teaspoon sugar
¼ teaspoon pepper
2 tablespoons minced parsley

Cut sprouts in half, lengthwise. Place in a saucepan with the water, salt, sugar, pepper and minced parsley. Bring to a boil, then cover and simmer for 5 minutes, or until sprouts are tender.
Serves 4. About 36 calories per serving.

APPLE BEETS

1 can (1 pound) whole beets, drained
1 can (1 pound) applesauce, unsweetened
1 tablespoon brown sugar
⅛ teaspoon salt
⅛ teaspoon nutmeg

Drain beets. Put applesauce in a saucepan and add sugar, salt and nutmeg. Blend and heat. Add drained beets and heat until beets are thoroughly warmed.
Serves 6. About 63 calories per serving.

SWEET AND SOUR RED CABBAGE

⅔ cup vinegar
2 cups hot water
1 tablespoon brown sugar
½ teaspoon salt
1 medium head red cabbage, shredded
1 large apple, pared, cored and diced

In a medium skillet, heat vinegar, water, sugar and salt. Add cabbage and apple and cook, covered, over low heat until tender.
Serves 6. About 41 calories per serving.

SWEET AND SOUR CABBAGE

½ head cabbage
1 tablespoon brown sugar
2 tablespoons lemon juice
½ teaspoon salt
1 can tomatoes (16 ounces)
1 onion, sliced thin

Cut cabbage in wedges. Place in a saucepan with brown sugar, lemon juice, salt, tomatoes and onion. Simmer, covered, for about 20 minutes.
Serves 4. About 73 calories per serving.

CRISP BUTTERED CABBAGE

2 tablespoons butter
1 large head cabbage, shredded
1 teaspoon brown sugar
½ teaspoon grated lemon peel
2 tablespoons fresh lemon juice
½ teaspoon celery seed
½ teaspoon salt
¼ teaspoon pepper

Melt butter in a large skillet. Add shredded cabbage. Cover and cook, stirring occasionally, about 6 to 8 minutes, or until just tender. Add brown sugar, lemon peel, lemon juice, celery seed, salt and pepper. Stir and simmer for several minutes longer. Serve at once.
Serves 6. About 54 calories per serving.

PARSLEY CARROTS

1 can tiny whole carrots
   (16 ounces)
1 tablespoon chopped parsley

1 teaspoon brown sugar
¼ teaspoon pepper

Empty the carrots into a small saucepan. Add remaining ingredients. Heat.
Serves 4. About 41 calories per serving.

CARROTS WITH PINEAPPLE

1 can tiny whole carrots
   (16 ounces)
1 tablespoon brown sugar

1 can (8¾ ounces) pineapple
   tidbits, water-packed

Drain carrots, empty carrots into a small saucepan. Add sugar and pineapple tidbits, including juice. Stir and heat together. Serve hot.
Serves 4. About 64 calories per serving.

HERBED CARROTS

1 can sliced carrots (1 pound)
2 tablespoons
   finely chopped onion
1 tablespoon butter

1 teaspoon lemon juice
¼ teaspoon dried rosemary
½ teaspoon brown sugar
½ teaspoon chopped parsley

Sauté the chopped onion in butter. Add drained juice from carrots. Add lemon juice, rosemary, sugar and parsley. Heat and reduce volume of liquid by half. Add carrots and heat through. Serve at once.
Serves 4. About 62 calories per serving.

CAULIFLOWER WITH CHEESE

1 whole cauliflower
1 cup water
½ teaspoon sugar
½ teaspoon salt

1 ounce grated
   American cheese
1 teaspoon paprika

Place cauliflower in a deep saucepan. Add water, sugar and salt. Cover and cook until cauliflower is tender but firm. Pour off water. Leaving cauliflower in saucepan, sprinkle grated American cheese over top. Sprinkle paprika over cheese. Cover quickly, turning heat off for several moments until cheese has melted. Serve at once.
Serves 6. About 36 calories per serving.

BAKED CORN AND TOMATOES

1 cup canned corn
1 cup canned whole tomatoes
1 tablespoon chopped
   green pepper

1 tablespoon chopped onion
¼ teaspoon thyme
½ teaspoon sugar
2 tablespoons bread crumbs

Combine corn, tomatoes, green pepper and onion. Add thyme and sugar. Pour into a greased 1-quart casserole. Sprinkle top with bread crumbs. Bake in a 350 degree oven for 15 minutes. Serves 4. About 42 calories per serving.

BROILED MUSHROOMS

12 large mushrooms
½ teaspoon salt
¼ teaspoon pepper
½ teaspoon brown sugar
1 teaspoon chopped parsley
2 tablespoons sour cream

Remove stems from washed mushrooms and chop them fine in a chopping bowl. Add salt, pepper, brown sugar and parsley. Stir in sour cream. Fill the centers of the mushrooms. Broil for about 4 minutes.
Serves 6. About 28 calories per serving.

ORANGE RICE

1½ cups orange juice
2 teaspoons sugar
2 teaspoons butter
½ teaspoon salt
1⅓ cups Minute Rice

Bring orange juice, sugar, butter and salt to a boil in a saucepan. Stir in rice. Cover, remove from heat, let stand 5 minutes.
Serves 4. About 120 calories per serving.

PINEAPPLE RICE

1⅓ cups Minute Rice
½ teaspoon salt
⅔ cup drained canned crushed pineapple
1⅓ cups boiling water

Combine ingredients in saucepan. Mix just to moisten all rice. Cover, remove from heat, let stand 5 minutes. Fluff lightly with a fork.
Serves 4. About 89 calories per serving.

EASY CREAMED SPINACH

2 packages (10 ounces each) frozen chopped spinach
1 onion, finely minced
½ teaspoon salt
½ teaspoon sugar
1 can condensed cream of celery soup
¼ teaspoon nutmeg

Place frozen blocks of spinach in a large saucepan. Add 1 cup water. Add finely minced onion, salt and sugar. Cover and simmer until spinach is soft. Drain in a collander. Return spinach to empty saucepan and stir in undiluted cream of celery soup. Add nutmeg. Serve at once.
Serves 8. About 48 calories per serving.

BAKED ACORN SQUASH

2 acorn squash, about ½ pound each
2 teaspoons butter
½ teaspoon salt
¼ teaspoon pepper
2 teaspoons brown sugar

Cut squash in halves, lengthwise and scrape out seeds. Place upside down in a baking pan; pour in a half-inch of boiling water and bake in a 400 degree oven for 30 minutes. Turn over and put a half teaspoon of butter in each cavity. Sprinkle with salt and pepper. Sprinkle with brown sugar. Continue baking until squash is tender.
Serves 4. About 45 calories per serving.

ACORN SQUASH RINGS WITH SWEET PEAS

2 acorn squash
  (about 1½ pounds)
1 can (1 pound) green peas
1 teaspoon sugar

Slice acorn squash crosswise into 1-inch rings. Remove seeds. In a large skillet, in salted boiling water, cook squash rings, covered, until tender. Drain. Heat peas, add sugar, then drain. Heap peas into the center of each squash ring.
Serves 8. About 58 calories per serving.

STEWED TOMATOES

2 cans whole tomatoes
1 teaspoon sugar
1 teaspoon dried basil
1 tablespoon dried minced onion flakes

Empty tomatoes and juice into a saucepan. Add sugar, basil and onion flakes. Stir to blend. Simmer for 10 minutes. Serve hot.
Serves 6. About 36 calories per serving.

BROILED TOMATOES WITH DILL

2 large tomatoes
1 tablespoon dill
1 tablespoon sour cream
½ teaspoon sugar

Cut tomatoes in half. Place cut sides up on a broiler. Combine dill, sour cream and sugar. Spoon on top of tomatoes. Broil for 10 minutes. Serve immediately.
Serves 4. About 35 calories per serving.

BAKED TOMATOES WITH GREEN PEPPERS

4 large tomatoes
1 green pepper
1 tablespoon
 finely minced onion
1 teaspoon salt

¼ teaspoon pepper
1 teaspoon sugar
1 tablespoon mustard
2 tablespoons fine
 bread crumbs

Cut tomatoes in half and place halves on a flat baking pan. Remove seeds from pepper and chop very fine. Add onion. Sprinkle cut sides of tomatoes with salt, pepper, sugar and then spread with mustard. Top each tomato with the green pepper mixture. Sprinkle each with bread crumbs. Bake in a 375 degree oven for 15 minutes.
Serves 8. About 29 calories per serving.

BROILED TOMATOES PARMESAN

8 medium tomatoes
1 teaspoon sugar
Seasoned salt
1 tablespoon oregano

3 tablespoons grated
 Parmesan cheese
4 teaspoons low-calorie
 margarine

Wash tomatoes; cut very thin slice off blossom end of each so tomatoes will set level. Cut about ½-inch slice off stem end. Sprinkle cut tops of each tomato with sugar, seasoned salt and crushed oregano leaves. Top each with about 1 teaspoon Parmesan cheese; dot each with ½ teaspoon margarine. Place on a broiler pan. Broil 3 to 5 inches from heat, starting in a cold broiler compartment. Broil 8 to 10 minutes, or until nicely browned and bubbly.
Serves 8. About 42 calories per serving.

TOMATO-CORN CREOLE

1 package (10 ounce) white shoe peg corn frozen in butter sauce in cooking pouch
1 tablespoon butter
¼ cup diced green pepper
2 tablespoons chopped onion
1 can (8 ounce) tomatoes, undrained
1 teaspoon sugar

Slip pouch of white shoe peg corn into boiling water; bring water to a second boil and continue cooking 12 minutes. Saute green pepper, and onion in butter until tender. Drain off excess butter. Stir in corn, tomatoes and sugar; heat through. Serves 6. About 112 calories per serving.

ZUCCHINI WITH FRESH LEMON BUTTER

2 pounds zucchini
Water
1 teaspoon salt
2 teaspoons boiling water
2 tablespoons sweet butter, softened
2 tablespoons fresh lemon juice
2 tablespoons instant minced onions
½ cup snipped parsley

Wash zucchini; slice into ¾-inch cartwheels. Cover bottom of broad frying pan with ¾ of an inch cold water; add salt and bring to a boil. Add zucchini; cover and cook just until tender, but still crisp, about 8 minutes. Drain thoroughly. While zucchini is cooking, add boiling water to softened butter. Mix well. Add lemon juice and whip mixture until smooth and creamy. Add onions and parsley. Pour mixture over drained zucchini. Serves 8. About 47 calories per serving.

ZUCCHINI-MUSHROOM DUET

2 pounds zucchini
½ pound fresh mushrooms
1 tablespoon butter
1 cup tomato juice
1 teaspoon monosodium glutamate
½ teaspoon salt
¼ teaspoon pepper
½ teaspoon brown sugar
¼ teaspoon thyme
½ teaspoon dried dillweed
2 tablespoons lemon juice

Slice zucchini into ⅛-inch discs. Slice mushrooms in thick slices, including stems. Melt butter in a large skillet. Toss in zucchini and mushroom slices. Sauté for several minutes. Add tomato juice and remaining seasonings. Stir and cover; simmer about 8 minutes.
Serves 8. About 46 calories per serving.

ZUCCHINI PARMESAN

2 pounds thinly sliced zucchini
1 onion, sliced thin
1 tablespoon butter
1 teaspoon dried dillweed
½ teaspoon monosodium glutamate
½ teaspoon brown sugar
½ teaspoon salt
¼ teaspoon thyme
2 tablespoons grated Parmesan cheese

In a large skillet, melt butter and toss in zucchini and onion slices. Add dillweed, monosodium glutamate, brown sugar, salt and thyme. Stir and cover. Simmer for 10 minutes, or until zucchini is tender. Sprinkle with Parmesan cheese and serve immediately.
Serves 8. About 43 calories per serving.

Corn Creole (page 63)
Photo courtesy of the Green Giant Company

Carrot Sesame Slaw (page 72)
Photo courtesy of the S&W Company

CHAPTER 8

SLENDER SALADS

These crisp salads are intended as side dishes for your dinner meal, or you may double a portion for your lunch. A variety of easy to prepare low-calorie dressings are included to add zesty taste to the merest lettuce leaf.

No need to skip the amenities of dining while dieting, if the calorie-counting has been done for you. Dieting does not mean starvation; it means learning to eat wisely.

CELERY SEED DRESSING

½ cup plain yogurt
2 tablespoons ketchup
1 teaspoon sugar
2 tablespoons lemon juice

1 tablespoon grated onion
½ teaspoon paprika
½ teaspoon celery seed

Stir ketchup into yogurt. Add sugar, lemon juice and grated onion. Add paprika and celery seed. Blend well. About 10 calories per tablespoon.

DRESSING FOR FRUIT SALADS

3 tablespoons vinegar
1 envelope Good Seasons Salad Dressing Mix

2 tablespoons salad oil
⅔ cup unsweetened pineapple juice

Place vinegar in cruet. Add salad dressing mix. Shake well. Then add oil and juice. Shake again. Arrange fruit on greens. Just before serving, shake dressing and then pour over fruit. Makes about 1 cup.
About 22 calories per tablespoon.

ITALIAN DRESSING

¼ cup wine vinegar
2 tablespoons lemon juice
1 tablespoon olive oil
1 clove garlic, crushed

1 teaspoon sugar
¾ teaspoon oregano
1 teaspoon salt
¼ teaspoon pepper

Combine all ingredients together in a tightly closed jar. Shake vigorously and let stand at least a half hour before using. About 20 calories per tablespoonful.

HERB DRESSING

1 can tomato sauce (8 ounces)
2 tablespoons tarragon vinegar
1 teaspoon
  Worcestershire sauce
1 teaspoon sugar
½ teaspoon salt
½ teaspoon basil
1 tablespoon grated onion

Combine all ingredients in a blender. Refrigerate until ready to use.
About 8 calories per tablespoon.

LEMON FRENCH DRESSING

1 teaspoon unflavored gelatin
1 tablespoon cold water
¼ cup boiling water
2 tablespoons sugar
½ teaspoon salt
1 teaspoon grated lemon peel
½ cup fresh lemon juice
¼ teaspoon garlic salt
⅛ teaspoon pepper
⅛ teaspoon dry mustard
¼ teaspoon
  Worcestershire sauce

Soften gelatin in cold water. Add boiling water and stir until gelatin dissolves. Stir in sugar and salt until dissolved. Combine mixture with remaining ingredients in a container with a tight fitting lid; shake well. Serve cool, but not chilled, over crisp salad greens. May be covered and stored in refrigerator until needed. If refrigerated, before serving time place container of dressing in pan of hot water for 5 minutes to reliquefy the gelatin. Makes about 1 cup.
About 12 calories per tablespoon.

EXTRA LOW-CALORIE DRESSING FOR FRUIT SALAD

1 envelope unflavored gelatin
¼ cup cold water
½ cup boiling water
1 teaspoon sugar
1 teaspoon finely minced onion
¼ teaspoon curry powder
¼ teaspoon paprika
¼ cup fresh lemon juice

Soften gelatin in cold water; dissolve in boiling water. Add sugar, minced onion, curry powder, paprika and lemon juice. Chill. Serve on fruit salads.
Makes 1 cup. About 3 calories per tablespoon.

GRAPEFRUIT-GINGER MOLD

1 can (16 ounces) grapefruit sections, water-packed
1 envelope plain gelatin
2 teaspoons sugar
2 tablespoons lemon juice
1 cup chopped apple, with skins
1 tablespoon chopped crystallized ginger

Add enough water to grapefruit liquid to make 1¼ cups in all. Mix gelatin and add ½ cup of grapefruit liquid. Stir in sugar and heat over low flame until gelatin is dissolved. Remove from heat and stir in remaining liquid and lemon juice. Chill until the mixture thickens to the consistency of egg white. Fold in ginger, chopped apple and grapefruit sections and pour into mold. Chill and unmold.
Serves 6. About 57 calories per serving.

MANDARIN SALAD

1 cup mandarin oranges (canned), drained
½ head crisp lettuce
½ cucumber, sliced thin
2 scallions, sliced thin
2 tablespoons French dressing, homemade

Combine mandarin orange segments, torn up crisp lettuce, sliced cucumber and sliced scallions. Add dressing just before serving and toss well.
Serves 4. About 34 calories per serving.

Homemade French Dressing:
2 tablespoons wine vinegar
2 tablespoons lemon juice
1 tablespoon sugar
½ teaspoon salt
¼ teaspoon mustard
⅛ teaspoon pepper

Combine all ingredients in a small jar, cover and shake vigorously to mix well.
About 10 calories per tablespoon.

MUSHROOM SALAD

1 small head iceberg lettuce
1 tablespoon chopped chives
3 large mushrooms, sliced paper thin
1 tablespoon lemon juice

Tear up lettuce into a salad bowl. Add chopped chives. Slice fresh white mushrooms paper-thin into a separate bowl. Add lemon juice to mushrooms and stir gently to coat the slices. Add to salad greens. Use Lemon French Dressing (page 68). Serves 4. About 21 calories per serving, without dressing.

SPINACH SALAD

1 pound fresh spinach, well washed and drained
1 Bermuda onion, sliced thin
2 stalks celery, sliced thin, diagonally
2 hard-cooked eggs, sliced
½ teaspoon salt
¼ teaspoon pepper
¼ cup sour cream
1 tablespoon lemon juice
½ teaspoon Worcestershire sauce
½ teaspoon sugar

Dry spinach leaves well, discard any tough leaves. Tear into a salad bowl. Add onion, celery and eggs. Add salt and pepper and mix through. Combine sour cream, lemon juice, Worcestershire sauce and sugar. Pour over salad and mix lightly.
Serves 8. About 52 calories per serving.

ORANGE-SPINACH SALAD BOWL

¼ cup fresh lemon juice
½ cup fresh orange juice
½ teaspoon paprika
1 teaspoon seasoned salt
1 teaspoon garlic powder
⅛ teaspoon freshly ground black pepper
1 quart fresh spinach leaves, torn
1 quart lettuce leaves, torn
½ cup sliced radishes
2 oranges, peeled, cut into bite-sized pieces

In a jar, combine lemon juice, orange juice, paprika, seasoned salt, garlic powder and pepper. Cover tightly and shake thoroughly to blend. Arrange torn spinach leaves, lettuce, radishes and oranges in salad bowl. Shake dressing and pour over salad. Toss lightly. Serve at once.
Serves 6. About 39 calories per serving.

ASPARAGUS SALAD

1 can (10½ ounces)
  cut asparagus spears
½ head lettuce, shredded
2 tablespoons tomato juice

1 tablespoon lemon juice
½ teaspoon sugar
1 tablespoon grated onion
½ teaspoon oregano

Arrange asparagus on shredded lettuce. Combine tomato juice, lemon juice, sugar, grated onion and oregano, shaking vigorously. Pour over salad just before serving.
Serves 4. About 31 calories per serving.

SHRIMP DELUXE SALAD

1 cup elbow macaroni
½ cup dairy sour cream
¼ cup French-style
  salad dressing
¾ teaspoon salt
¼ teaspoon garlic salt
⅛ teaspoon seafood
  seasoning

Dash pepper
1 can (1 pound) sweet
  peas, drained
2 cups cooked shrimps, chilled
⅓ cup chopped celery
¼ cup chopped onion
¼ cup diced pimientos

Cook macaroni according to package directions; rinse in cold water. Mix sour cream, French dressing, salt, garlic salt, seafood seasoning and pepper. Fold in remaining ingredients. Toss all lightly together. Chill until ready to serve.
Serves 8. About 180 calories per serving.

KRAUT RELISH

1 can (1 pound) sauerkraut
2 tablespoons sugar
½ cup finely chopped celery
½ cup finely chopped green pepper
½ cup finely chopped carrot
¼ cup finely chopped onion

Cut sauerkraut into tiny pieces. Stir in sugar and let stand for a half hour. Add remaining ingredients. Cover bowl tightly and chill at least 12 hours before serving.
Serves 8. About 33 calories per serving.

CARROT SESAME SLAW

1 can (1 pound) julienne carrots, drained
2 cups shredded crisp raw cabbage
1 tablespoon green pepper, chopped
1 tablespoon onion, chopped
¼ cup sour cream
2 tablespoons mayonnaise
1 teaspoon lemon juice
1 teaspoon sugar
1 tablespoon toasted sesame seeds

Place carrots, cabbage, green pepper and onion in a salad bowl. Combine sour cream, mayonnaise, lemon juice and sugar; pour over carrot-cabbage mixture. Sprinkle with toasted sesame seeds.
Serves 8. About 64 calories per serving.

COLESLAW

1 pound of raw cabbage, shredded
1 small onion, sliced thin
¼ cup sour cream
2 tablespoons salad dressing (mayonnaise type)
1 teaspoon sugar
½ teaspoon salt
¼ teaspoon pepper
1 tablespoon vinegar
1 tablespoon celery seed

Combine shredded cabbage and sliced onion in a bowl. Combine separately sour cream, salad dressing, sugar, salt, pepper and vinegar. Blend well and mix through the cabbage. Refrigerate, covered, for several hours, stirring occasionally. Serves 6. About 60 calories per serving.

COLORFUL COLESLAW

1½ cups finely shredded green cabbage
1½ cups finely shredded red cabbage
1 cup shredded carrots
¼ cup salad dressing, mayonnaise-type
¼ cup sour cream
1 tablespoon vinegar
2 teaspoons sugar
½ teaspoon salt

Combine chilled shredded green and red cabbage. Add shredded carrots. Combine salad dressing, sour cream, vinegar, sugar and salt. Pour over vegetables and mix through. Refrigerate, covered, until serving time.
Serves 8. About 58 calories per serving.

VEGETABLE SALAD BOWL

1 clove garlic
1 head lettuce, about 2 pounds
1 cup spinach leaves
4 radishes, sliced thin
2 tomatoes, cut in eighths
2 carrots, sliced thin
½ head cauliflower, cut into small flowerets
1 Bermuda onion, sliced thin

Rub salad bowl with the cut side of garlic. Discard. Tear lettuce into bite-sized pieces. Cut membranes from spinach and tear leaves in bite-sized pieces; arrange around the edge of salad bowl. Place sliced radishes in center. Surround radishes with tomato wedges. Arrange carrot slices and cauliflower parts in a circle inside spinach ring. Toss thin slices of separated onion around edge. Use one of the low calorie dressings, such as Celery Seed Dressing on page 64.
Serves 8. About 43 calories per serving, without dressing.

CAULIFLOWER SALAD

1 cup sliced raw cauliflower
2 tomatoes, diced
2 tablespoons chopped chives
1 head lettuce, shredded
Lemon French Dressing
(page 68)

Combine sliced cauliflower and diced tomatoes. Pour ¼ cup Lemon French Dressing over the vegetables and mix through. Let stand in refrigerator for an hour or so. When ready to serve, combine with chopped chives and lettuce.
Serves 6. About 34 calories per serving, with dressing.

PICKLED CUCUMBERS WITH DILL

2 cucumbers
1 onion
½ cup white vinegar
2 teaspoons sugar

1 teaspoon salt
¼ teaspoon pepper
1 tablespoon chopped dill
¼ cup cold water

Peel cucumbers and slice paper thin. Place in a deep small bowl. Slice onions paper thin and separate into single slices. Add to cucumbers. In a tall glass, stir vinegar, sugar, salt, pepper, dill and water. Pour over cucumbers and mix through. Cover and refrigerate for several hours, or overnight.
Serves 6. About 28 calories per serving.

CRANBERRY-VEGETABLE ASPIC MOLD

2 tablespoons unflavored gelatin
2 cups cranberry juice cocktail
2 cups apple juice
2 tablespoons lemon juice

1 small onion, grated
1 cup ground fresh cranberries
1 cup strained cooked sliced carrots
1 cup sliced raw celery

Sprinkle gelatin over ½ cup cranberry juice. Let stand 5 minutes to soften. Stir over low heat until gelatin is dissolved. Add remaining cranberry juice, apple juice and lemon juice. Blend well. Chill until thickened. Fold in remaining ingredients. Pour mixture into 2-quart mold. Chill until firm. Unmold and garnish with crisp salad greens.
Serves 8. About 87 calories per serving.

PINEAPPLE-CUCUMBER RING

2 tablespoons unflavored gelatin
¼ cup cold water
1 can (1 pound) crushed pineapple, water-packed
2 cucumbers, pared
¼ cup lemon juice
2 tablespoons sugar
Green food coloring

Soften gelatin in cold water. Strain pineapple, reserving syrup. Chop cucumbers and combine with pineapple. Add lemon juice to pineapple syrup and add water to make 2 cups. Heat liquid and stir in gelatin mixture. Add sugar and a few drops of food coloring to achieve a pale green color. Chill in refrigerator until mixture thickens to the consistency of raw egg white. Fold in pineapple-cucumber mixture. Pour into a greased 1-quart ring mold and return to refrigerator. Chill until firm and ready to serve. Unmold on salad greens.
Serves 8. About 45 calories per serving.

FRUIT SALAD MOLD

1 package (3 ounces) orange gelatin
1 cup boiling water
1 cup cold water
1 orange, sectioned and diced
1 small banana, sliced
1 small red apple, diced
⅓ cup thinly-sliced celery

Dissolve gelatin in boiling water. Add cold water. Chill ⅓ in mold until almost set. Chill rest of gelatin until slightly thickened; fold in fruit and celery. Pour into mold. Chill until firm. Serves 6. About 88 calories per serving.

EASY TOMATO ASPIC

1 can (10 ounces) tomato juice
1 package (3 ounces) lemon gelatin
½ teaspoon salt
Dash of pepper
1½ tablespoons lemon juice

Heat 1 cup tomato juice to a boil. Stir in gelatin until dissolved. Stir into rest of juice in can. Add salt, pepper and lemon juice. Chill in can until firm. Puncture bottom of can, dip in warm water, unmold. To serve, cut into slices.
Serves 8. About 56 calories per serving.

VEGETABLE SALAD MOLD

1 package lemon gelatin
1 cup boiling water
1 cup cold water
¾ teaspoon salt
Dash of pepper
2 tablespoons vinegar
2 teaspoons grated onion
½ cup diced celery
1½ cups raw grated carrot

Dissolve gelatin in boiling water. Add cold water and seasonings. Fold in onion, celery and carrot. Pour into 6 molds. Chill until firm. Unmold.
Serves 6. About 72 calories per serving.

ASPARAGUS SPEAR SALAD MOLD

1 can (15 ounces) asparagus spears
1½ teaspoons salt
1½ tablespoons vinegar
4 thin pimiento rings
1 package (3 ounces) lemon gelatin
1½ teaspoons grated onion

Drain asparagus; add water to liquid to make 1½ cups. Add salt and vinegar; bring to a boil. Then arrange asparagus in 4 clusters in a 9 x 5-inch pan. Place pimiento over each cluster. Dissolve gelatin in boiling liquid; add onion. Pour over asparagus. Chill until firm.
Serves 4. About 105 calories per serving.

CORN RELISH MOLD

1 package (3 ounces) lemon gelatin
1½ teaspoons salt
¾ cup boiling water
1 can (1 pound) kernel corn
½ cup sweet pickle relish
1 tablespoon chopped pimiento

Dissolve gelatin and salt in boiling water. Add corn, relish and pimiento. Pour into a small loaf pan. Chill until firm. To serve, cut in slices and use in place of a vegetable with roasts or cold meat platters.
Serves 10. About 78 calories per serving.

CHAPTER 9

EDUCATED EGGS

Trickily packed in their own sanitary containers, eggs provide a low-calorie source of protein for those who are watching their weight. They are a perfect product to use in imaginative ways beyond the usual boiling and scrambling. Watch them puff up into appetizing omelets, as you add the bits of flavor that make each recipe unique. Use them for breakfast or lunch in the tempting dishes devised for your delight!

STRAWBERRY SOUR CREAM OMELET

5 eggs, separated
¼ cup sour cream
½ teaspoon salt
½ teaspoon pepper

½ cup sliced fresh strawberries
1 tablespoon powdered sugar

Beat yolks. Add sour cream, salt and pepper. Beat egg whites stiff; fold into yolk mixture. Using a teflon-lined pan, pour mixture into pan and cook at low heat on top of stove until omelet is set. Then place pan in a 350 degree oven for 10 minutes, or until omelet is firm. Lift out on a platter with care. Arrange sliced berries quickly over the top and sprinkle with powdered sugar. Break apart with two forks to serve.
Serves 3. About 180 calories per serving.

PUFFED EGGS

8 eggs, separated
¼ teaspoon cream of tartar
½ teaspoon salt
¼ teaspoon pepper

½ teaspoon sugar
2 teaspoons grated Parmesan cheese
2 tablespoons chopped chives

Beat yolks until thick and lemon colored. Add salt, pepper, sugar, grated Parmesan cheese and chives. Beat whites until soft peaks form. Add cream of tartar and beat until stiff. Fold whites into yolk mixture and pour into a casserole. Bake at 350 degrees about 20 minutes, or until firm. Serve at once.
Serves 6. About 110 calories per serving.

MUSHROOM OMELET

3 eggs
1 tablespoon milk
¼ teaspoon salt

1 can (8 ounces) sliced mushrooms
1 tablespoon lemon juice
½ teaspoon brown sugar

Beat eggs, milk and salt together. Pour into a teflon-lined skillet, cover and turn the heat low. Meanwhile, empty mushrooms and juice into a small saucepan; add lemon juice and brown sugar and heat through. Remove omelet from pan when fully set. Fill one half with mushrooms, removing them from the saucepan with a slotted spoon. Flip over other half of omelet and cut in half.
Serves 2. About 150 calories per serving.

EGGS FLORENTINE

1 package frozen, chopped spinach, cooked
½ teaspoon brown sugar
¼ teaspoon nutmeg

1 teaspoon lemon juice
3 eggs
1 tablespoon Parmesan cheese
½ teaspoon paprika

Drain spinach. Stir in sugar, nutmeg, lemon juice. Spoon spinach into 3 individual baking dishes. Break an egg into each dish, being careful to keep yolk whole. Sprinkle Parmesan cheese and paprika over eggs. Bake in a 400 degree oven for 15 minutes, or until egg is set. Serve at once.
Serves 3. About 109 calories per serving.

ZUCCHINI OMELET

1 zucchini
2 tablespoons butter
½ teaspoon salt
¼ teaspoon pepper
½ teaspoon brown sugar

⅛ teaspoon thyme
6 eggs
2 tablespoons grated Parmesan cheese
½ teaspoon oregano

Wash zucchini and cut in slices, about ⅛-inch thick. Melt butter in a skillet, toss in slices of zucchini and season with salt, pepper, sugar and thyme. Simmer for several minutes, until zucchini is softened. Beat eggs lightly, add grated cheese and oregano. Pour over zucchini and cook on low heat until eggs are set, covering if necessary.
Serves 6. About 119 calories per serving.

EGGS IN TOMATOES

1 cup (canned) whole peeled tomatoes
1 tablespoon finely chopped onion

2 eggs
Pinch of dill
8 canned asparagus spears

Place onions, tomatoes and dill in a shallow baking pan and bake in a 350 degree oven for 10 minutes. Break eggs carefully on top of tomato mixture. Spread asparagus spears decoratively between eggs. Bake at 350 degrees until whites of eggs are thickened. Serve at once.
Serves 2. About 114 calories per serving.

SCRAMBLED ASPARAGUS

½ cup asparagus spears,
   cut up
6 eggs
1 tablespoon butter

¼ teaspoon salt
⅛ teaspoon pepper
½ teaspoon sugar

Add unbeaten eggs to asparagus spears and mix gently through. Heat butter in a skillet, pour in egg mixture, season with salt, pepper and sugar and stir gently while eggs become firm. Serve immediately.
Serves 6. About 100 calories per serving.

EGG SALAD MOLDS

1 tablespoon (1 envelope)
   unflavored gelatin
¼ cup salad dressing
   (mayonnaise-type)
1½ cups hot bouillon
½ teaspoon sugar
¾ teaspoon salt

¼ teaspoon saffron
6 hard-cooked eggs, *chopped*
½ cup diced celery
1 can (1 pound) small
   early peas, drained
2 tablespoons diced pimiento

Stir gelatin into salad dressing in medium mixing bowl. Gradually blend in hot bouillon using electric or rotary beater. Stir in sugar, salt, saffron; chill until slightly thickened. Fold in remaining ingredients; pour into oiled 4-ounce salad molds. Chill until firm. Unmold on water cress or salad greens.
Serves 10. About 104 calories per serving.

COTTAGE CHEESE OMELET

4 eggs, separated
1 cup cottage cheese, creamy style
½ teaspoon salt
¼ teaspoon pepper
1 teaspoon vanilla flavoring
1 tablespoon butter

Beat yolks until lemon colored. Add cottage cheese, salt, pepper and vanilla. Beat whites until stiff peaks form. Fold whites into yolk mixture. Melt butter in a skillet. Pour in egg mixture and cook over low heat until bottom edges are lightly browned. Then bake in a 350 degree oven for about 15 minutes, or until omelet is firm. Serve at once.
Serves 4. About 160 calories per serving.

RANCH OMELET

3 eggs, beaten
1 tablespoon milk
2 tablespoons green pepper, diced fine
2 tablespoons chives, chopped
2 tablespoons pimiento, diced
¼ teaspoon salt
⅛ teaspoon pepper

Add milk to beaten eggs. Add diced pepper, chives and pimiento. Add salt and pepper. Pour into a heated teflon-lined skillet. Cover and cook until set. Flip onto platter.
Serves 2. About 123 calories per serving.

Egg Salad Molds (page 83)
Photo courtesy of the Green Giant Company

Bacon and Egg Divan (page 90)
Photo courtesy of the Green Giant Company

CHAPTER 10

SLIM SANDWICHES

Sandwiches in a diet? Why not, if the extra calories are sliced out as they are in these recipes, and you are left with a mouthful of good eating, as you whittle your weight.

Included in this chapter are many open-faced treats that are hot off the griddle. They are designed to please your palate and your scale!

OPEN—FACED BEEFWICH

6 slices white bread
¾ pound lean ground beef
1 tablespoon finely minced
  onion
½ teaspoon salt
¼ teaspoon pepper
½ teaspoon mustard
1 teaspoon soy sauce

Combine beef with onion, salt, pepper, mustard and soy sauce. Spread thinly on each slice of bread. Broil for about 4 minutes, or until done to degree of rareness preferred. Serves 6. About 174 calories per serving.

BROILED CHEESE TREAT

1 slice white bread
2 tablespoons cottage cheese
1 teaspoon brown sugar
½ teaspoon cinnamon

Spread cottage cheese over the slice of bread. Sprinkle with brown sugar and cinnamon. Slip under the broiler for about 3 minutes. Serve at once.
103 calories each.

GRILLED CHEESE AND TOMATO

1 slice bread
1 slice American cheese
1 thick slice tomato
¼ teaspoon brown sugar
¼ teaspoon basil
½ teaspoon Parmesan cheese

Top bread with American cheese and then with tomato. Sprinkle top of tomato with brown sugar, basil and Parmesan cheese. Slip under the broiler for 3 minutes, or until cheese is melted.
About 152 calories each.

DEVILED CRABWICH

4 slices bread
1 can (3 ounces) crabmeat
1 tablespoon parsley, *chopped*
1 tablespoon relish
2 tablespoons tomato sauce

Arrange bread on a broiling pan. Combine crabmeat, parsley, relish and tomato sauce. Spoon over bread in a thin layer. Slip under the broiler for 4 minutes. Serve at once.
Serves 4. About 125 calories per serving.

SARDINE PUFF

4 slices bread
12 sardines
1 egg, separated
2 tablespoons sour cream
½ teaspoon Worcestershire sauce

Arrange bread on a broiling pan. Place 3 sardines on each slice of bread. Beat yolk lightly; add sour cream and Worcestershire sauce. Beat egg white until stiff; fold into yolk batter. Spoon over sardines. Bake in a 350 degree oven for 12 minutes, or until lightly browned and puffed.
Serves 4. About 134 calories per serving.

TOMATO-CHEESEWICH

1 slice white bread
2 slices tomato
1 ounce shredded American cheese
¼ teaspoon oregano

Arrange tomato slices on the bread. Top with shredded cheese and oregano. Broil until cheese is melted.
About 175 calories each.

ASPARAGUS SANDWICH PUFF

6 slices bread, toasted
1 can (1 pound)
 stewed tomatoes, drained
6 slices processed
 pimiento cheese

1 can (1 pound) asparagus
 spears, drained
3 eggs, separated
½ teaspoon sugar
⅛ teaspoon salt
⅛ teaspoon pepper

Drain tomatoes and spoon over toast slices. Top with slices of cheese and then with asparagus spears. Beat egg yolks until lemon colored. Add sugar, salt, and pepper. Beat egg whites until stiff and combine with yolk mixture. Spoon egg mixture over asparagus and bake in a moderate oven of 350 degrees for about 15 minutes.
Serves 6. About 207 calories per portion.

AMERICAN PIZZA

4 English muffins, split
½ cup tomato sauce
1 tablespoon oregano

2 slices American cheese
3 tablespoons grated
 Parmesan cheese

Arrange 8 pieces of English muffins on a cookie sheet. Spoon tomato sauce on each, and spread to the edges. Sprinkle with oregano. Cut American cheese in quarters and place a square in the center of the tomato sauce. Sprinkle with Parmesan cheese. Slip under the broiler for 4 minutes, or until cheese is melted. Serve at once.
Makes 8 pizzas. About 92 calories each.

SALMON ON THE HALF SHELL

4 hamburger rolls, cut in half
1 can (7 ounces) salmon, sockeye
1 tablespoon chopped chives
8 thick slices beefsteak tomatoes
1 teaspoon sugar
½ teaspoon salt
2 tablespoons Parmesan cheese

Cut buns in half and scoop out excess bread, forming a shell. Tear up this excess bread and combine it with the salmon. Add chopped chives and spoon into center of each bun. Place one slice of tomato on each bun. Sprinkle with sugar, salt and Parmesan cheese. Place under the broiler for 3 minutes, or until cheese is melted.
Serves 8. About 122 calories per serving.

SWISS CLAM BUN

1 can (3 ounces) minced clams, drained
4 hamburger buns, halved
4 slices Swiss cheese, chopped
1 tablespoon chopped green pepper
½ teaspoon Worcestershire sauce

Empty clams in a strainer and drain. Cut buns in half and scoop out extra bread. Combine bread with clams, tearing bread into bits. Stir Worcestershire sauce through chopped Swiss cheese; add chopped green pepper. Spoon cheese mixture over clams. Slip under a broiler for 3 minutes, or until cheese is melted. Serves 8. About 116 calories per serving.

TUNA BURGER

4 hamburger rolls
1 can (7 ounces) tuna fish, water-packed
¼ cup grated carrot
¼ cup finely diced celery

½ tablespoon sour cream
½ tablespoon salad dressing, mayonnaise-type
½ teaspoon sugar
1 teaspoon lemon juice

Slice rolls in half. Mash tuna fish; combine with grated carrot, diced celery. Stir together sour cream, salad dressing, sugar and lemon juice. Blend through the tuna mixture. Spoon mixture on buns.
Serves 4. About 231 calories per bun.

BACON AND EGG DIVAN

2 packages (10 ounces each) broccoli frozen in cheese sauce in cooking pouches
12 tomato slices

6 hard-cooked eggs, quartered
6 slices buttered toast, cut in half
6 slices bacon
1 teaspoon brown sugar

Slip frozen cooking pouches of broccoli in cheese sauce into about 3 cups boiling water; bring to a second boil; cook 18 minutes, turn several times to insure complete cooking. Do not cover pan. Towards end of cooking time, arrange tomato slices and eggs on toast triangles on serving plates. Fry bacon crisply; drain and sprinkle with brown sugar; fry until sugar has melted. Place half of each bacon slice across each toast triangle; open pouches and pour broccoli over all. Serve two triangles to each portion.
Serves 6. About 220 calories per serving.

CHAPTER 11

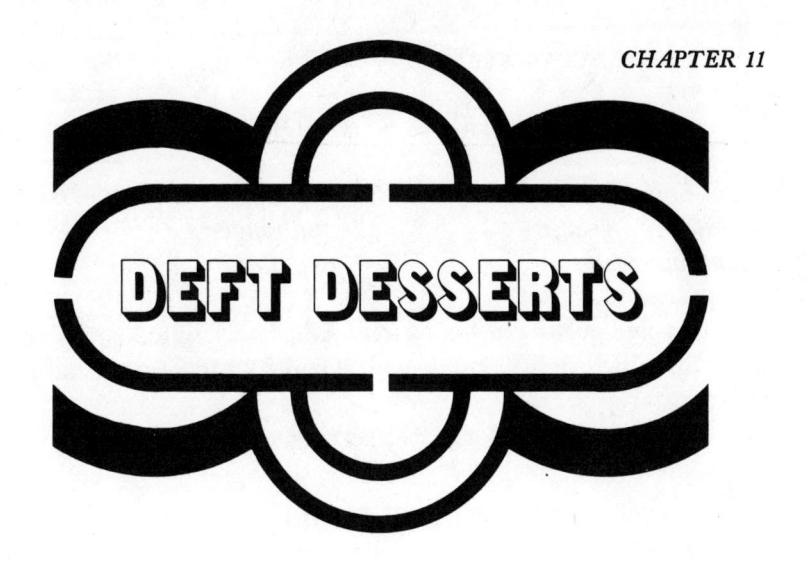

DEFT DESSERTS

Skip dessert? Not in this book! Choose a recipe to end your dinner with a treat from these low-calorie ideas. The portions are small, but if properly served in stemmed glasses, they will provide a sweet ending to your dinner experience.

No need to leave the table with an unfulfilled sweet tooth, when you can prepare the slender satisfiers that perk up your energy without destroying your diet!

SPARKLING PEAR DESSERT

1 package (3 ounces) raspberry gelatin
1 cup hot water
1½ teaspoons lemon juice
1 cup ginger ale
1 cup diced pears

Dissolve gelatin in hot water. Add lemon juice and ginger ale. Chill until slightly thickened. Then fold in pears. Chill until firm.
Serves 6. About 93 calories per serving.

GRAPE FLUFF

2 tablespoons brown sugar
½ cup sour cream
1 pound seedless green grapes
Nutmeg

Combine brown sugar and sour cream. Remove stems from grapes and toss with sour cream mixture. Divide into four sherbet glasses. Dash nutmeg over each. Serve cold.
Serves 4. About 88 calories per serving.

ORANGE SNOW

1 envelope (1 tablespoon) unflavored gelatin
½ cup sugar
¼ teaspoon salt
1¼ cups hot water
1 can (6 ounces) frozen concentrated orange juice, thawed
2 egg whites, unbeaten

Dissolve gelatin, sugar and salt in hot water. Add juice. Chill until slightly thickened. Then place in bowl set in ice water. Add egg whites and beat to soft peaks. Chill until firm.
Serves 8. About 92 calories per serving.

APRICOT FLUFF

1 jar (5 ounces)
   strained apricots for babies
1 tablespoon sugar
1 teaspoon vanilla
1 teaspoon lemon juice

1 teaspoon grated lemon rind
1 tablespoon cold water
1 teaspoon unflavored gelatin
2 egg whites

Stir strained apricots, sugar, vanilla, lemon juice and lemon rind together. Soften gelatin in the cold water, then dissolve over hot water in a double boiler. Beat egg whites until frothy; add gelatin and beat very stiff. Fold into apricot mixture and put into sherbet glasses. Chill.
Serves 4. About 54 calories per serving.

FRESH ORANGE FREEZE

4 medium oranges
1 teaspoon sugar
½ cup fresh orange juice

1 bottle (12 ounces)
   low-calorie, lemon-lime,
   carbonated beverage

Peel oranges; slice into cartwheels. Sprinkle with sugar and chill. Meanwhile, combine orange juice and carbonated beverage. Pour into shallow pan and place in freezer. Freeze until crystals form on bottom of pan. Stir mixture and continue to freeze until partially frozen and slushy. Quickly transfer to a chilled bowl and whip with electric beater at high speed until smooth. Or place into electric blender; cover and blend at high speed until smooth. Spoon into serving dishes and top with chilled, sugared, orange slices. Serve at once, garnishing with fresh mint, if desired.
Serves 4. About 89 calories per serving.

FRESH LEMON ANGEL FLUFF

4 egg yolks
½ cup sugar
1 teaspoon grated lemon peel
⅓ cup fresh lemon juice
4 egg whites
¼ teaspoon cream of tartar

Combine egg yolks and sugar in top of double boiler. Beat with electric beater until eggs are thick and lemon colored. Place over simmering water; add lemon peel and lemon juice very gradually, beating constantly. Cook mixture, continuing to beat, until very thick and fluffy. Turn into bowl immediately and refrigerate until chilled. Beat egg whites until frothy; add cream of tartar and beat at high speed until whites are stiff but not dry. Carefully fold beaten whites into chilled egg yolk mixture. Spoon mixture into parfait or sherbet glasses. Chill thoroughly. Serves 6. About 109 calories per serving.

PINEAPPLE-GRAPE SHERBET

1 can (6 ounces) frozen, unsweetened, pineapple juice concentrate
3½ cups cold water
2 tablespoons sugar
1 can (6 ounces) frozen, unsweetened, grape juice concentrate
1 cup nonfat dry milk solids

Empty juice concentrates into a mixing bowl. Add water, sugar and dry milk. Beat until blended thoroughly. Pour into two ice cube trays; freeze 1 or 2 hours until half frozen. Empty into a large chilled mixing bowl; beat on low speed until mixture is softened, then beat on high speed 3 to 5 minutes until mixture is creamy but not liquid. Pour into freezer containers or ice cube trays. Freeze until ready to serve.
Makes 20 half-cup servings. About 71 calories per serving.

FRESH LEMON ICE

½ envelope unflavored gelatin
½ cup sugar
¾ cup water
3 egg whites

1 tablespoon grated lemon peel
½ cup fresh lemon juice

In a small saucepan, thoroughly combine gelatin and ¼ cup sugar. Blend in water, stirring until smooth. Bring mixture to a boil, stirring until gelatin is dissolved. Remove from heat. Beat whites at high speed until soft peaks form; add remaining sugar gradually, continuing to beat until all sugar is used and whites are stiff, but not dry. Continue beating, adding warm mixture in a thin, steady stream. Beat in grated lemon peel and juice. Pour into ice-cube trays or shallow baking pan; freeze until mushy, stirring once or twice.

When mixture is evenly frozen to the mushy stage, transfer to chilled mixing bowl. With chilled beaters, beat at high speed until smooth and light. Spoon immediately into lemon shells or serving dishes. Freeze until firm.
Serves 8. About 65 calories per serving.

SHERRY AMBROSIA

8 Navel oranges, peeled
⅓ cup flaked coconut

1 teaspoon powdered sugar
1½ ounces sherry

Slice peeled oranges into cartwheels; arrange in serving dish in layers. Combine flaked coconut with powdered sugar and top oranges with the coconut. Chill. Just before serving, sprinkle with sherry.
Serves 8. About 84 calories per serving with sherry.
About 78 calories per serving without sherry.

STRAWBERRY FLIP

1 cup sliced strawberries
2 tablespoons sour cream

1 teaspoon brown sugar
Nutmeg

Divide strawberries into 2 sherbet glasses. Place a tablespoon of sour cream atop each. Sprinkle brown sugar and a dash of nutmeg over sour cream. Serve cold.
Serves 2. About 57 calories per serving.

EASY BAKED APPLES

4 baking apples
4 teaspoons brown sugar

4 teaspoons raisins

Core apples. Place each apple on doubled squares of aluminum foil. Fill each with a teaspoon of brown sugar and a teaspoon of raisins. Seal foil tightly. Place in a pan and bake in a 400 degree oven for 45 minutes. Can serve hot or cold.
Serves 4. About 93 calories per serving.

FRUIT COMPOTE

1 can (16 ounces) apricots, water-packed
1 can (16 ounces) peaches, water-packed

1 medium sized orange, juice and rind, grated
½ lemon, juice and rind, grated
1 teaspoon honey

Drain apricot and peach juice into a saucepan. Add orange and lemon juices and rinds. Add honey. Heat thoroughly, reducing volume of liquid. Pour over fruit and chill.
Serves 6. About 70 calories per serving.

FRUIT AMBROSIA

1 package (12 ounces) frozen mixed fruit
½ teaspoon brown sugar
1 teaspoon lemon juice
¼ cup flaked coconut

Remove block of fruit from carton. Place in bowl and let stand at room temperature until just thawed, about 2½ hours. Add brown sugar, lemon juice and coconut. Mix gently. Spoon into sherbet glasses.
Serves 4. About 136 calories per serving.

SPANISH CREAM

1 envelope unflavored gelatin
6 tablespoons sugar, divided
⅛ teaspoon salt
2 eggs, separated
2 cups milk, divided
1 teaspoon vanilla

Mix together gelatin, 2 tablespoons of the sugar, and salt in saucepan. Beat together egg yolks and 1 cup of the milk; add to the gelatin mixture. Place over low heat, stirring constantly, until gelatin is dissolved and mixture is slightly thickened, about 5 minutes. Remove from heat; add remaining 1 cup milk and vanilla. Chill until mixture mounds slightly when dropped from a spoon. Beat egg whites until stiff, but not dry. Gradually add remaining 4 tablespoons sugar and beat until very stiff. Fold into gelatin mixture. Turn into a 4-cup mold, or 8 individual 4-ounce molds. Chill until firm. Unmold and serve with dollops of fruit or sauce.
Serves 8. About 100 calories per serving.

PEARS IN CLARET

1 can (16 ounces) pears, water-packed
½ cup claret wine
Few broken pieces of stick cinnamon

Place all ingredients in saucepan and heat thoroughly. Pick out pieces of cinnamon and serve immediately.
Serves 5. About 45 calories per serving.

PEARS MELBA

4 halves of canned pears, water-packed
2 cups vanilla ice cream
½ cup frozen raspberries

Arrange a pear half in each of 4 sherbet glasses. Place ½ cup of ice cream on each pear. Put raspberries in a blender, or thaw and sieve, to get a smooth sauce. Pour over ice cream. Serve at once.
Serves 4. About 129 calories per serving.

PEARS IN GIN

1 can (16 ounces) pears, water-packed
1 cup canned grapefruit, drained
5 teaspoons honey
2 tablespoons gin

Pour juice from pears into baking dish and place pears, hollow side up, in dish. Mash grapefruit and spoon pulp into hollow of pears. Drop teaspoonsful honey onto grapefruit. Bake in a preheated oven at 400 degrees until thoroughly heated. Heat gin in separate pan or ladle, ignite and pour over pears.
Serves 5. About 80 calories per serving.

MAPLED PEARS

1 can (16 ounces) pears, drained, water-packed
½ cup maple-flavored syrup
Pinch of nutmeg
2 tablespoons chopped pecans

Combine maple-flavored syrup and nutmeg; simmer pear halves in syrup for 5 minutes; cool in syrup and chill. Top with pecans.
Serves 5. About 35 calories per serving.

CITRUS FLAVORED YOGURT

2 cups plain yogurt
1 tablespoon grated orange rind
1 tablespoon grated lemon rind
1 tablespoon chopped fresh mint

Combine all ingredients and mix well. Chill.
Serves 4. About 73 calories per serving.

GINGER YOGURT

2 cups plain yogurt
1 tablespoon chopped crystalized ginger
1 tablespoon brown sugar

Combine ingredients and mix well. Chill.
Serves 4. About 105 calories per serving.

MAPLE-NUT YOGURT

2 cups plain yogurt
1 tablespoon maple-flavored syrup
1 tablespoon chopped pecans
1 tablespoon lime juice

Combine all ingredients and mix well. Chill. Serves 4. About 98 calories per serving.

SPICED HONEY YOGURT

2 cups plain yogurt
1 tablespoon honey
¼ teaspoon cinnamon
⅛ teaspoon nutmeg

Combine all ingredients and mix well. Chill. Serves 4. About 86 calories per serving.

Spanish Cream (page 97)
Photo courtesy of Knox

Pears Helene Pie (page 105)
Photo courtesy of Kellogg Company

CHAPTER 12

CONTROLLED CAKES

All cakes cannot be used by dieters, except in near-invisible portions, but many can. Count your blessings and count your calories from this group of easy-to-bake cakes that barely remind you of your diet. To remove all temptations for a second slice, you can divide your cakes into portions and freeze them. Remove a slice from the freezer before dinner and it will be ready when you are!

Bake a jar full of these low-calorie cookies and you will always be prepared to serve thin desserts. Here is a treasury of guiltless recipes!

LEMON ANGEL CAKE

1 package Angel Food
   Cake Mix
3 tablespoons cornstarch
⅔ cup sugar
Dash of salt
1 cup water

1 tablespoon margarine
⅓ cup concentrated
   frozen lemonade
Yellow food coloring
1 teaspoon vanilla

Prepare cake mix according to package directions. Cool; then split to make 2 layers.

Mix cornstarch, sugar, salt. Stir in cold water. Cook and stir over medium heat until thickened and clear, about 5 minutes. Remove from heat. Add margarine, lemonade, several drops yellow food coloring and vanilla. Stir until well blended. Chill. Spread between layers.
Serves 12. About 183 calories per serving.

COFFEE SPONGE CAKE

5 eggs, separated
1 cup sugar
1 tablespoon lemon juice
½ cup strong coffee

1½ cups sifted cake flour
½ teaspoon baking powder
¼ teaspoon salt
¾ teaspoon cream of tartar

Preheat oven to 325 degrees. Beat egg yolks until thick and lemon colored. Add sugar, lemon juice and coffee; beat until thick and fluffy, about 10 minutes. Sift together flour, baking powder and salt; carefully fold into egg yolk mixture. Beat egg whites until foamy; add cream of tartar and beat until stiff peaks form. Fold egg yolk mixture gently into whites; pour into a 9-inch tube pan. Bake at 325 degrees 45 to 50 minutes.
Serves 12. About 141 calories per slice.

CONTROLLED CAKES

LEMON SPONGE CAKE

4 eggs
1 cup sugar
¾ cup sifted flour
1 teaspoon baking powder

2 tablespoons lemon juice
1 tablespoon grated lemon rind

Separate eggs. Beat yolks until lemon colored. Add sugar gradually. Add flour, baking powder, lemon juice and lemon rind. Beat egg whites until stiff, adding a pinch of salt while beating to increase volume. Carefully fold whites into the batter. Grease bottom of a 10-inch, angel-food, tube pan and sprinkle bottom with a small amount of confectionary sugar. Pour batter into prepared pan and bake in a 350 degree oven for 40 minutes, or until lightly browned. Remove from oven and invert until cool.
Serves 12. About 113 calories per serving.

ORANGE SPONGE CAKE

4 eggs
1 cup sugar
⅔ cup orange juice

1 cup flour
1 teaspoon baking powder

Separate eggs. Beat yolks until lemon colored. Add sugar and beat three minutes. Add juice. Add sifted flour and baking powder. Beat egg whites in a separate bowl until stiff, adding a pinch of salt during the start of beating to increase volume. Fold beaten whites into batter. Bake in an ungreased angel-food tin at 325 degrees for 40 minutes, or until lightly browned. Remove from oven and invert pan to cool.
Serves 12. About 126 calories per serving.
Or bake in layers and frost with chocolate Whip 'N Chill prepared mix. Add 40 calories per serving.

WALNUT SPONGE ROLL

4 eggs, separated
½ teaspoon salt
1 teaspoon vanilla
½ cup sugar

¼ cup sifted enriched flour
¼ cup chopped walnuts
1 package Whip 'N Chill, vanilla

Beat egg whites with salt and vanilla, until soft peaks form. Beat in sugar. Beat egg yolks separately until thick. Add flour and walnuts. Fold yolk mixture into whites. Line bottom and sides of a jelly-roll pan with waxed paper. Spread batter evenly in the pan. Bake in a 375 degree oven for 12-15 minutes. Cool for several minutes, then turn out onto a towel. Peel off paper and roll up. Cool. Prepare Whip 'N Chill with water, according to directions on package, using ¼ less water than directed. Unroll sponge layer, spread with ¾ of whipped mixture, and roll up again. Spread remaining ¼ of whipped mixture over top. Serves 10. About 138 calories per serving.

QUICK-AND-EASY COFFEE CAKE

2 packages refrigerated biscuits
2 tablespoons melted butter
2 tablespoons brown sugar

2 tablespoons finely chopped pecans
2 tablespoons grated orange rind

Grease a round ring mold. Unwrap refrigerated biscuits and separate. Dip each biscuit carefully in melted butter and then in a mixture of the brown sugar, chopped pecans and grated orange peel. Place them one by one, overlapping as you go, in the greased ring mold. Bake in a 400 degree oven for about 20 minutes, or until lightly browned. Invert and sprinkle with a light dusting of confectionary sugar if desired.
Serves 10. About 129 calories per serving.

RASPBERRY CHIFFON PIE

1 tablespoon
  unflavored gelatin
¼ cup cold water
3 eggs, separated
½ cup sugar

⅛ teaspoon salt
1 tablespoon lemon juice
2 cups fresh red raspberries
1 9-inch baked pie shell

    Soften gelatin in cold water, dissolve over boiling water. Combine egg yolks, sugar and salt. Beat on high speed of mixer. Add lemon juice. Crush and strain ½ cup of raspberries. Add slowly to egg mixture in the top of a double boiler; cook, stirring constantly, until slightly thickened. Stir in dissolved gelatin; chill until mixture begins to set. Beat egg whites until stiff peaks form; fold into thickened gelatin along with the remaining berries. Pour into baked pie shell; chill until set.
Serves 6. About 232 calories per serving.

PEARS HELENE PIE

¾ cup packaged
  corn flake crumbs
2 tablespoons sugar
2 tablespoons soft or
  melted butter

1 quart vanilla ice cream,
  slightly softened
8 chilled canned pear halves,
  packed in water
Shaved chocolate

    Combine corn flake crumbs, sugar and butter in 9-inch pie pan; mix well. Press evenly and firmly around sides and bottom of pie pan. Chill. When crust is firm, spread with softened ice cream; freeze until ice cream is firm. Before serving, arrange pear halves, cut side down, over ice cream. Sprinkle with small amount of shaved chocolate. Cut in wedges to serve.
Serves 8. About 225 calories per serving.

CHOCOLATE CREAM ROLL

6 eggs, separated
½ cup sugar
6 tablespoons dry cocoa

1 teaspoon vanilla
1 package Whip 'N Chill, vanilla

Grease jelly-roll pan and line with waxed paper. Lightly grease the waxed paper. Heat oven to 350 degrees. Beat egg yolks until thick and lemon colored. Add sugar. Add cocoa and vanilla. Beat egg whites until stiff, adding a pinch of salt while beating to increase volume. Carefully fold egg whites into batter. Spread evenly in prepared jelly-roll pan and bake for 25 minutes, or until firm. Remove from oven and invert pan on a clean dish towel. Remove pan. Gently remove waxed paper. Roll cake into shape while still warm and set aside to cool. When cool unroll and spread with prepared Whip 'N Chill dessert product, made with water instead of milk according to the directions on the package, using ¼ less water than directed. Roll up again.
Serves 10. About 139 calories per serving.

PEACH COBBLER PIE

1 package (8 ounces) frozen peach slices, thawed
¼ teaspoon cinnamon
¼ cup sifted flour

¼ cup sugar
¼ teaspoon salt
2 tablespoons butter

Arrange thawed peach slices in a 9-inch pie pan. Sprinkle with cinnamon. Sift flour, sugar and salt into a bowl. Add butter and cut up until mixture is mealy. Spoon over peach slices. Bake at 400 degrees for 30 minutes, or until top is crisp. Serve warm or cold.
Serves 6. About 128 calories per serving.

APPLESAUCE MERINGUE

⅛ teaspoon salt
4 egg whites
1 cup granulated sugar
½ teaspoon vinegar
¾ teaspoon vanilla
⅓ cup slivered almonds
2 cups unsweetened applesauce

Add salt to egg whites; beat stiff, but not dry. Add sugar, about 1 tablespoon at a time and beat well after each addition. Beat in vinegar and vanilla. Fold in ½ of the almonds. Cover a cookie sheet with waxed paper and form egg white mixture into a circle, about 8 inches in diameter. Shape the outer two inches of the circle about one inch higher than the rest. If preferred, make individual ovals of egg mixture and make depression in each with the back of a spoon. Bake in a very slow 250 degree oven for about 50 minutes. Remove to serving platter with spatula. Cool. Fill depression with applesauce and sprinkle with remaining slivered almonds.
Serves 12. About 108 calories per serving.

COCONUT MERINGUE COOKIES

4 egg whites
½ teaspoon salt
½ cup sugar
1 teaspoon almond extract
½ cup coconut flakes

Beat egg whites and salt until soft peaks form. Add sugar gradually while beating until mixture is stiff. Add almond extract and coconut. Drop by spoonfuls onto a well greased cookie sheet. Bake for about 40 minutes in a 250 degree oven, then turn off heat. Let oven cool before removing cookies. Store in covered cannister. Makes about 3 dozen.
About 23 calories per cookie.

CRANBERRY COOKIES

½ cup sifted flour
¼ teaspoon salt
½ teaspoon baking soda
1 teaspoon cinnamon
¼ teaspoon nutmeg
⅛ teaspoon cloves
⅛ teaspoon all spice

½ cup rolled oats
½ cup raisins
½ cup cranberry sauce
¼ cup salad oil
1 unbeaten egg
1 teaspoon vanilla

Sift flour, salt, soda and spices together; add rolled oats and raisins. Combine cranberry sauce, salad oil, egg and vanilla. Stir into dry ingredients till moistened. Drop by teaspoonfuls on a lightly greased cookie sheet. Bake in a 375 degree oven for 10 to 12 minutes.
Makes about 2 dozen cookies. About 54 calories each.

LOW-FAT BRAN MUFFINS

¾ cup sifted flour
2½ teaspoons baking powder
¼ teaspoon salt
2 tablespoons sugar
1 egg, well beaten

¾ cup skim milk
1 tablespoon salad oil
1½ cups Post
   Bran Flakes, 40%

Mix flour, baking powder, salt and sugar. Combine egg and skim milk. Add to flour mixture; add salad oil and mix only enough to dampen flour. Fold in cereal. Lightly grease muffin pans. Spoon the batter into pans filling each about two-thirds full. Bake in a 425 degree oven for 15 to 20 minutes.
Makes 8 medium sized muffins. About 105 calories per muffin.

CHAPTER 13

CALORIE COUNT

DAIRY PRODUCTS

CHEESES:

American, Cheddar type	115	1 oz.
	70	1" cube
	225	½ cup, grated
Process American, Cheddar type	105	1 oz.
Blue-mold (Roquefort)	105	"
Cottage, not creamed	25	2 tbsps.
Cottage, creamed	30	"
Cream Cheese	105	"
Parmesan, dry, grated	40	"
Swiss	105	1 oz.

FLUID MILK:

Whole	165	1 cup
Skim	90	"
Buttermilk	90	"
Evaporated (undiluted)	170	½ cup
Condensed, sweetened (undiluted)	490	"
Half-and-half (milk and cream)	330	1 cup
	20	1 tbsp.

MILK BEVERAGES:

Cocoa (all milk)	235	1 cup
Chocolate-flavored Milk Drink	190	"
Chocolate Milk Shake	520	12 oz.
Malted Milk	280	1 cup

OTHERS:

Butter	100	1 tbsp.
Cream, light	35	"
Cream, heavy whipping	55	"
Ice Cream, plain	130	3½ oz.
Ice Cream Soda, chocolate	455	1 glass
Ice Milk	140	½ cup
Yogurt (partially skimmed milk)	120	1 cup

MEATS & POULTRY
(Cooked, without bone)

BEEF:

Pot Roast or Braised
   Lean and fat .... 245 ..... 3 oz.
   Lean only .... 140 ..... 2½ oz.
Oven Roast
   Lean and fat .... 220 ..... 3 oz.
   Lean only .... 130 ..... 2½ oz.
Steak, broiled
   Lean and fat .... 330 ..... 3 oz.
   Lean only .... 115 ..... 2 oz.
Hamburger
   Regular ground beef .... 245 ..... 3 oz. patty
   Lean ground round .... 185 .....   "
Corned Beef, canned .... 180 ..... 3 oz.
Corned Beef Hash, canned .... 120 .....   "
Dried Beef, chipped .... 115 ..... 2 oz.
Meat Loaf .... 115 .....   "
Beef and Vegetable Stew .... 90 ..... ½ cup
Beef Potpie, baked .... 460 ..... 1 pie, 4¼" dia.

VEAL:

Cutlet, broiled (meat only) .... 185 ..... 3 oz.

CHICKEN:

Broiled .... 185 ..... 3 oz.
Fried .... 215 ..... ½ breast
                                      245 ..... Thigh and drumstick
Canned .... 190 ..... ½ cup

LAMB:

Chop
    Lean and fat .... 405 ..... 4 oz.
    Lean only .... 140 ..... 2-3/5 oz.
Roast Leg
    Lean and fat .... 235 ..... 3 oz.
    Lean only .... 130 ..... 2½ oz.

PORK:

Chop
    Lean and fat .... 260 ..... 2⅓ oz.
    Lean only .... 130 ..... 2 oz.
Roast Loin
    Lean and fat .... 310 ..... 3 oz.
    Lean only .... 175 ..... 2-2/5 oz.
Ham, Cured
    Lean and fat .... 290 ..... 3 oz.
    Lean only .... 125 ..... 2-1/5 oz.
Bacon, broiled .... 95 ..... 2 thin slices

SAUSAGE & VARIETY MEATS:

Bologna Sausage .... 170 ..... 2 oz.
Liver Sausage .... 175 ..... "
Vienna Sausage, canned .... 135 ..... "
Pork Sausage, bulk .... 170 ..... 2 oz. patty
Beef Liver, fried .... 120 ..... 2 oz.
Beef Tongue, boiled .... 205 ..... 3 oz.
Frankfurter .... 155 ..... Each
Boiled Ham .... 170 ..... 2 oz.
Spiced Ham, canned .... 165 ..... "

FISH & SHELLFISH

Bluefish, baked	135	3 oz.
Clams, shelled		
Raw, meat only	70	"
Canned, clams & juice	45	"
Crab Meat	90	"
Fish Sticks	200	4 oz.
Haddock, fried	135	3 oz.
Mackerel		
Broiled	200	"
Canned	155	"
Ocean Perch, fried	195	"
Oysters, raw	80	6 to 10
Salmon		
Broiled	205	4 oz.
Canned (pink)	120	3 oz.
Sardines, canned in oil	180	"
Shrimp, canned	110	"
Tuna, canned in oil	170	"

EGGS

Fried	100	1 large
Boiled	80	"
Scrambled or Omelet	110	"
Poached	80	"

NUTS

Almonds, shelled	105	15 nuts
Brazil Nuts, broken	115	2 tbsps.
Cashew Nuts, roasted	95	5 nuts
Coconut, shredded	40	2 tbsps.
Peanuts, roasted, shelled	105	"
Peanut Butter	90	1 tbsp.
Pecans, shelled	90	12 halves
Walnuts, shelled		
Black	100	2 tbsps.
English	80	10 halves

VEGETABLES

Asparagus	20	6 spears
Beans, fresh		
Lima	75	½ cup
Snap, Green or Wax	15	"
Beans, dried		
Red Kidney, cooked	115	"
Lima, cooked	130	"
Baked		
With pork	165	"
Without pork	160	"
Beets	35	"
Beet Greens, cooked	20	"
Broccoli	20	"
Brussels Sprouts	30	"

Cabbage
   Raw .... 10..... "
   Coleslaw (with dressing) .... 50..... "
   Cooked .... 20..... "
Carrots .... 20..... "
Cauliflower .... 15..... "
Celery .... 10..... 2 large stalks
Chard .... 25..... ½ cup
Collards .... 40..... "
Corn, cooked .... 85..... ½ cup
Cress, Garden .... 35..... "
Cucumbers .... 5..... 6 slices
Kale .... 20..... ½ cup
Kohlrabi .... 25..... "
Lettuce .... 5..... 3 leaves
Mushrooms, canned .... 15..... ½ cup
Mustard Greens .... 15..... "
Okra, cooked .... 15..... 4 pods
Onions
   Raw .... 50..... 1 medium size
   Cooked .... 40..... ½ cup
Parsnips, cooked .... 50..... "
Peas, Green .... 60..... "
Peppers, Green .... 15..... 1 medium
Potatoes
   Baked or boiled .... 90..... "
   Chips .... 110..... 10 medium
   French Fried .... 155..... 10 pieces
   Hash-browned .... 235..... ½ cup
   Mashed with milk .... 70..... "
   Pan fried .... 240..... "
Radishes .... 10..... 4 small
Sauerkraut, canned .... 15..... ½ cup

Spinach .... 20..... "
Squash
  Summer .... 20..... "
  Winter, baked .... 50..... "
Sweet Potatoes
  Baked .... 155..... 1 medium
  Canned .... 120..... ½ cup
Tomatoes
  Raw .... 30..... 1 medium
  Cooked or canned .... 25..... ½ cup
Tomato Juice .... 25..... "
Turnips, cooked .... 20..... "
Turnip greens .... 20..... "

FRUITS

Apples, raw .... 70..... 1 medium
Apple Juice .... 60..... ½ cup
Applesauce
  Sweetened .... 90..... "
  Unsweetened .... 50..... "
Apricots
  Raw .... 55..... 3
  Canned, water pack .... 45..... ½ cup
  Canned, syrup pack .... 110..... "
  Dried, cooked,
    unsweetened .... 120..... "
  Frozen, sweetened .... 125..... "
Avocados .... 185..... ½ 10-oz. size
Bananas, raw .... 85..... 1 medium

Berries
  Blackberries, raw .... 40 ..... ½ cup
  Blueberries, raw .... 45 ..... "
  Raspberries, raw .... 35 ..... "
    Frozen, sweetened .... 120 ..... "
  Strawberries, raw .... 30 ..... "
    Frozen, sweetened .... 120 ..... "
Cantaloupe, raw .... 40 ..... ½ melon, 5" dia.
Cherries
  Raw .... 30 ..... ½ cup
  Canned red, sour, pitted .... 55 ..... "
Cranberry Sauce, sweetened .... 30 ..... 1 tbsp.
Cranberry Juice Cocktail .... 70 ..... ½ cup
Dates .... 250 ..... "
Figs
  Raw .... 90 ..... 3 small
  Canned, heavy syrup .... 110 ..... ½ cup
  Dried .... 60 ..... 1 large
Fruit Cocktail,
  canned in syrup .... 100 ..... ½ cup
Grapefruit
  Raw .... 50 ..... ½ medium
  Canned water pack .... 35 ..... ½ cup
  Canned syrup pack .... 80 ..... "
Grapefruit Juice
  Unsweetened .... 50 ..... "
  Sweetened .... 65 ..... "
Grapes .... 45 ..... 3½ oz.
Grape Juice, bottled .... 75 ..... ½ cup
Honeydew Melon .... 50 ..... 2" x 7" wedge
Lemon Juice .... 30 ..... ½ cup
                                  5 ..... 1 tbsp.

GENERAL CALORIE COUNTS

Lemonade	65	½ cup
Oranges, raw	70	1 orange
Orange Juice	60	½ cup
Peaches		
Raw	35	1 medium
Canned, water pack	40	½ cup
Canned, syrup pack	100	"
Dried, cooked, unsweetened	110	"
Frozen, sweetened	105	"
Pears		
Raw	100	1 pear
Canned in heavy syrup	100	½ cup
Pineapple		
Raw	35	½ cup, diced
Canned, syrup pack	100	½ cup or 2 slices
Pineapple Juice	60	½ cup
Plums		
Raw	30	1 plum
Canned syrup pack	90	½ cup
Prunes, dried cooked		
Unsweetened	150	9 prunes
Sweetened	260	"
Prune Juice, canned	85	½ cup
Raisins, dried	230	"
Rhubarb, cooked, sweetened	190	"
Tangerine, raw	40	1 medium
Tangerine Juice, canned	50	½ cup
Watermelon, raw	120	4" x 8" wedge

BREADS AND CEREALS

Cracked wheat	60	slice
Raisin	60	"
Rye	55	"
White	60	"
Whole Wheat	55	"

OTHER BAKED GOODS

Baking Powder Biscuit	130	each
Graham Crackers	55	2 medium
Saltines	35	2
Soda Crackers	45	2
Plain Muffins	135	each
Bran Muffins	125	"
Corn Muffins	155	"
Pancakes, wheat	60	4" dia.
Buckwheat Cakes	45	"
Pizza (cheese)	180	⅛, 14" pie
Pretzels	20	5 sticks
Plain Pan Rolls	115	each
Hard Round Rolls	160	"
Sweet Pan Rolls	135	"
Rye Wafers	45	2
Waffles	240	4½" x 5½"

CEREALS AND OTHER GRAIN PRODUCTS

Bran Flakes (40% bran)	85	1 oz.
Corn, puffed, presweetened	110	"
Corn and Soy Shreds	100	"
Corn Flakes	110	"
Corn Grits, cooked	90	¾ cup
Farina, cooked	80	"
Macaroni, cooked	115	"
Macaroni and Cheese	240	½ cup
Noodles, cooked	150	¾ cup
Oat Cereal	115	1 ounce
Oatmeal, cooked	110	¾ cup
Rice, cooked	150	"
Rice Flakes	115	1 cup
Rice, Puffed	55	"
Spaghetti, cooked	115	¾ cup
Spaghetti with Meat Sauce	215	"
Spaghetti in Tomato Sauce, with Cheese	160	"
Wheat, Puffed	100	1 oz.
Wheat, Puffed, presweetened	105	"
Wheat, Rolled, cooked	130	¾ cup
Wheat, Shredded, plain	100	1 oz.
Wheat Flakes	100	¾ cup
Wheat Flours		
Whole wheat	300	"
All-purpose flour	300	¾ cup sifted
Wheat germ	185	¾ cup

FATS, OILS, AND RELATED PRODUCTS

Margarine ....100.....1 tbsp.
Cooking Fats
   Vegetable ....110..... ”
   Lard ....135..... ”
Salad or Cooking Oils ....125..... ”

SALAD DRESSINGS

French .... 60.....1 tbsp.
Blue Cheese, French .... 90..... ”
Home-cooked, boiled .... 30..... ”
Low-calorie .... 15..... ”
Mayonnaise
   Home-cooked ....110..... ”
   Commercial .... 60..... ”
Thousand Island .... 75..... ”

CANDY, SYRUPS, JAMS, JELLY

Caramels ....120.....1 oz.
Chocolate Creams ....110..... ”
Chocolate, Milk, sweetened ....145.....1 oz. bar
Chocolate, Milk, sweetened,
   with almonds ....150..... ”
Chocolate Mints ....110.....1 oz.

GENERAL CALORIE COUNTS

Fudge, Chocolate	115	"
Gumdrops	95	"
Hard Candy	110	1 oz.
Jelly Beans	65	"
Marshmallows	90	"
Peanut Brittle	125	"
Chocolate Syrup	40	1 tbsp.
Honey	60	"
Molasses, Cane, light	50	"
Syrup, table blends	55	"
Jelly	50	"
Jam, Marmalade, Preserves	55	"
Sugar	18	1 tsp.

DESSERTS

Apple Betty	175	½ cup
Angel Food Cake	110	2" Sector
Butter Cake, plain	180	3" x 2" x 1½" slice, or
	130	cupcake
Chocolate Cake, with fudge icing	420	2" piece
Doughnut	135	each
Fruitcake, dark	105	2" x 2" x ½" slice
Gingerbread	180	"
Pound Cake	130	1" slice
Sponge Cake	115	2" piece
Cookies, plain	110	3" dia.

Cornstarch Pudding	140	½ cup
Custard, baked	140	"
Fig Bars, small	55	each
Fruit Ice	75	½ cup
Gelatin dessert, plain	80	"
Pies		
Apple	330	4" piece
Cherry	340	"
Custard	265	"
Lemon Meringue	300	"
Mince	340	"
Pumpkin	265	"
Prune Whip	100	½ cup
Rennet Dessert Pudding	125	"
Sherbet	120	"

BEVERAGES

Ginger Ale	80	8-oz. glass
Kola type	105	"
Low-calorie type	10	"
Postum	5	1 cup
Coffee or Tea	0	"
Beer, 4% alcohol	175	12 oz.
Whiskey, gin, rum:		
100-proof	125	1½ oz.
90-proof	110	"
86-proof	105	"
80-proof	100	"
70-proof	85	"
Wines, table use	70	3 oz.
Sweet Wines	120	"

CHAPTER 14

THREE WEEKS OF DELICIOUS DINING FOR LESS THAN 1000 CALORIES DAILY

FIRST DAY

BREAKFAST:
CALORIES

½ cup orange juice	60
Soft boiled egg	80
Coffee, 1 teaspoon sugar	18

LUNCHEON:

*Crabmeat Divan (Page 24)	128
Wedge of Lettuce	10
*Home-made French Dressing (Page 69)	10
Coffee or tea, 1 teaspoon sugar	18

DINNER:

*Beef Egg Drop Soup (Page 20)	22
*Flank Steak Teriyaki (Page 37)	365
*Orange Rice (Page 59)	120
*Marinated Beans (Page 52)	34
*Fresh Lemon Angel Fluff (Page 94)	109
Coffee or tea, 1 teaspoon sugar	18
	992

SECOND DAY

	CALORIES
BREAKFAST:	
½ cup pineapple juice	60
*Broiled Cheese Treat (Page 86)	103
Coffee, 1 teaspoon sugar	18
LUNCHEON:	
*Mushroom Omelet (Page 81)	150
Lettuce, shredded	10
*Herb Dressing (Page 67)	8
Coffee or tea, 1 teaspoon sugar	18
DINNER:	
*Asparagus Bisque (Page 16)	42
*Zesty Meat Loaf (Page 39)	319
*Cauliflower With Cheese (Page 59)	36
*Pineapple Cucumber Ring (Page 76)	45
*Chocolate Cream Roll (Page 106)	139
Coffee or tea, 1 teaspoon sugar	18
	966

THIRD DAY

BREAKFAST: CALORIES

½ cup orange juice	60
Poached Egg on one-half English muffin	135
Coffee, 1 teaspoon sugar	18

LUNCHEON:

*Open-faced Beefwich (Page 86)	174
*Asparagus Salad (Page 71)	131
Coffee or tea, 1 teaspoon sugar	18

DINNER:

*Broiled Grapefruit (Page 8)	63
*Oven-Fried Chicken Parmesan (Page 32)	251
*Baked Corn and Tomatoes (Page 58)	42
*Zucchini with Fresh Lemon Butter (Page 63)	47
One slice bread	60
*Pears in Claret (Page 98)	45
Coffee or tea, 1 teaspoon sugar	18
	962

FOURTH DAY

CALORIES

BREAKFAST:

½ cup grapefruit juice	60
1 slice toast, topped with	60
1 slice American cheese	105
Coffee, 1 teaspoon sugar	18

LUNCHEON:

*Banana Ambrosia (Page 8)	68
*Eggs Florentine (Page 81)	109
Coffee or tea, 1 teaspoon sugar	18

DINNER:

*Shrimp Gumbo (Page 17)	49
*Sweet And Sour Lamb Chops (Page 43)	207
*Baked Acorn Squash (Page 60)	45
*Broiled Tomatoes With Dill (Page 61)	35
*Mushroom Salad (Page 69)	21
*Lemon French Dressing (Page 67)	12
*Coffee Sponge Cake (Page 102)	141
Coffee or tea, 1 teaspoon sugar	18
	966

FIFTH DAY

BREAKFAST: CALORIES

½ fresh orange, sliced	37
1 poached egg, on	80
1 slice toast	60
Coffee, 1 teaspoon sugar	18

LUNCHEON:

*Shrimp Sauté (Page 25)	107
*Asparagus Spear Salad Mold (Page 78)	105
Coffee or tea, 1 teaspoon sugar	18

DINNER:

*Spinach Soup (Page 19)	27
*Savory Veal Roast (Page 48)	251
*Crisp Buttered Cabbage (Page 56)	54
*Zippy Green Beans (Page 51)	16
*Apple Beets (Page 55)	63
*Peach Cobbler Pie (Page 106)	128
Coffee or tea, 1 teaspoon sugar	18
	982

SIXTH DAY

BREAKFAST:

	CALORIES
½ cup pineapple juice	60
*Cottage Cheese Omelet (Page 84)	160
Coffee, 1 teaspoon sugar	18

LUNCHEON:

*Banana Sole Amandine (Page 28)	129
*Easy Tomato Aspic (Page 77)	56
Coffee or tea, 1 teaspoon sugar	18

DINNER:

*Sherry Consomme (Page 20)	63
*Chicken Rosemary (Page 35)	232
*Parsley Carrots (Page 57)	41
*Pineapple Rice (Page 59)	89
*Fresh Orange Freeze (Page 93)	89
Coffee or tea, 1 teaspoon sugar	18
	973

SEVENTH DAY

BREAKFAST:

	CALORIES
½ grapefruit	75
1 cup puffed rice	42
½ cup milk	75
Coffee, 1 teaspoon sugar	18

LUNCHEON:

*Asparagus Sandwich Puff (Page 88)	207
Coffee or tea, 1 teaspoon sugar	18

DINNER:

*Tomato Bouillon (Page 18)	29
*Boiled Beef With Dill Sauce (Page 41)	361
*Sweet And Sour Red Cabbage (Page 55)	41
*Green Beans And Tomatoes (Page 52)	38
*Pineapple-Grape Sherbet (Page 94)	71
Coffee or tea, 1 teaspoon sugar	18
	993

EIGHTH DAY

	CALORIES

BREAKFAST:

½ cup orange juice	60
Soft boiled egg	80
1 slice toast	60
Coffee, 1 teaspoon sugar	18

LUNCHEON:

*Broiled Fish Parmesan (Page 30)	108
*Island Green Beans (Page 53)	57
Coffee or tea, 1 teaspoon sugar	18

DINNER:

*Vegetable Clam Broth (Page 19)	30
*Meatball Stew (Page 40)	368
*Orange-Spinach Salad Bowl (Page 70)	39
*Walnut Sponge Roll (Page 104)	138
Coffee or tea, 1 teaspoon sugar	18
	994

NINTH DAY

BREAKFAST: CALORIES

½ cup grapefruit juice   60
1 egg, scrambled in teflon pan   80
1 slice toast   60
Coffee, 1 teaspoon sugar   18

LUNCHEON:

*Cucumber-Cream Broiled Fillets (Page 29)   114
*Vegetable Salad Bowl (Page 74)   43
*Celery Seed Dressing (Page 66)   10
Coffee or tea, 1 teaspoon sugar   18

DINNER:

*Corn Chowder (Page 18)   69
*Savory Minute Steaks (Page 43)   363
*Asparagus Au Gratin (Page 50)   36
*Baked Tomatoes With Green Peppers (Page 62)   29
*Apricot Fluff (Page 93)   54
Coffee or tea, 1 teaspoon sugar   18

                                                       972

TENTH DAY

CALORIES

BREAKFAST:

½ fresh orange, sliced	37
1 cup cream of wheat cereal, with	100
1 teaspoon raisins, and	12
½ cup skim milk	45
Coffee, 1 teaspoon sugar	18

LUNCHEON:

*Tomato-Cheesewich (Page 87)	175
*Kraut Relish (Page 72)	33
Coffee or tea, 1 teaspoon sugar	18

DINNER:

½ cup tomato juice	25
*Curried Lamb Stew (Page 44)	284
*Brussels Sprouts (Page 55)	36
Wedge of lettuce	10
*Herb Dressing (Page 67)	8
*Pears Melba (Page 98)	129
Coffee or tea, 1 teaspoon sugar	18
	948

ELEVENTH DAY

BREAKFAST: CALORIES

½ cup pineapple juice   60
1 soft boiled egg   80
1 slice toast   60
Coffee, 1 teaspoon sugar   18

LUNCHEON:

*American Pizza (Page 88)   92
*Cole Slaw (Page 73)   60
Coffee or tea, 1 teaspoon sugar   18

DINNER:

*Jellied Tomato Soup With Sherry (Page 19)   32
*Stuffed Flank Steak (Page 39)   238
*Acorn Squash Rings With Sweet Peas (Page 61)   58
*Corn Relish Mold (Page 78)   78
*Lemon Angel Cake (Page 102)   183
Coffee or tea, 1 teaspoon sugar   18
                                                    ———
                                                    995

TWELFTH DAY

BREAKFAST:
                                                                 CALORIES

½ cup orange juice	60
1 cup cold wheat flakes, with	125
½ cup skim milk	45
Coffee, 1 teaspoon sugar	18

LUNCHEON:

*Salmon On The Half Shell (Page 89)	122
Lettuce wedge	10
*Italian Dressing (Page 66)	20
Coffee or tea, 1 teaspoon sugar	18

DINNER:

*French Onion Soup (Page 22)	62
*Potted Chicken With Artichoke (Page 33)	242
*Zucchini Parmesan (Page 63)	43
*Herbed Carrots (Page 57)	62
*Fruit Ambrosia (Page 97)	136
Coffee or tea, 1 teaspoon sugar	18
	981

THIRTEENTH DAY

	CALORIES
BREAKFAST:	
½ grapefruit	50
1 slice toast, topped with	60
1 slice Swiss cheese (1 ounce)	105
Coffee, 1 teaspoon sugar	18

LUNCHEON:

*Broiled Swordfish With Barbecue Sauce (Page 27)	127
*Broiled Tomatoes Parmesan (Page 62)	42
Coffee or tea, 1 teaspoon sugar	18

DINNER:

*Gazpacho (Page 18)	65
*Herbed Burgers (Page 40)	232
*Sweet And Sour Cabbage (Page 56)	73
*Mandarin Salad (Page 69)	34
*Homemade French Dressing (Page 69)	10
*Easy Baked Apple (Page 96)	93
Coffee or tea, 1 teaspoon sugar	18
	945

FOURTEENTH DAY

BREAKFAST: **CALORIES**

½ cup pineapple-grapefruit juice   60
½ cup puffed wheat   42
½ cup skim milk   45
Coffee, 1 teaspoon sugar   18

LUNCHEON:

*Ranch Omelet (Page 84)   123
*Pickled Cucumbers With Dill (Page 75)   28
Coffee or tea, 1 teaspoon sugar   18

DINNER:

*Puree Mongol Soup (Page 20)   77
*Shrimp Stew (Page 26)   170
½ cup cooked rice   100
*Spinach Salad (Page 70)   52
*Raspberry Chiffon Pie (Page 105)   232
Coffee or tea, 1 teaspoon sugar   18
                                                          ───
                                                          983

FIFTEENTH DAY

	CALORIES
BREAKFAST:	
½ cup orange juice	60
1 soft boiled egg	80
1 slice toast	60
Coffee, 1 teaspoon sugar	18
LUNCHEON:	
*Deviled Crabwich (Page 87)	125
*Colorful Coleslaw (Page 72)	58
Coffee or tea, 1 teaspoon sugar	18
DINNER:	
*Tomato-Rice Soup (Page 17)	45
*Swiss Steak (Page 37)	333
*Asparagus Vinaigrette (Page 50)	32
*Carrots With Pineapple (Page 57)	64
*Fresh Lemon Ice (Page 95)	65
Coffee or tea, 1 teaspoon sugar	18
	976

SIXTEENTH DAY

	CALORIES
BREAKFAST:	
½ cup grapefruit juice	60
1 cup puffed rice, with	42
½ sliced banana, and	43
½ cup skim milk	45
Coffee, 1 teaspoon sugar	18
LUNCHEON:	
*Zucchini Omelet (Page 82)	119
*Cranberry Vegetable Aspic Mold (Page 75)	87
Coffee or tea, 1 teaspoon sugar	18
DINNER:	
*Cockaleekie Soup (Page 21)	45
*Leg of Lamb Au Café (Page 46)	235
*Green Beans and Tomatoes (Page 52)	38
Baked Potato	90
*Cauliflower Salad (Page 74)	34
*Spiced Honey Yogurt (Page 100)	86
Coffee or tea, 1 teaspoon sugar	18
	978

SEVENTEENTH DAY

BREAKFAST:
CALORIES

½ fresh orange, sliced	37
*Puffed Eggs (Page 80)	110
Coffee, 1 teaspoon sugar	18

LUNCHEON:

*Tuna Burger (Page 90)	231
Lettuce wedge with wine vinegar	10
Coffee or tea, 1 teaspoon sugar	18

DINNER:

*Crabmeat Bisque (Page 16)	87
*Veal Strogonoff (Page 47)	251
*Easy Creamed Spinach (Page 60)	48
*Grapefruit Ginger Mold (Page 68)	57
*Coconut Meringue Cookies (4) (Page 107)	92
Coffee or tea, 1 teaspoon sugar	18
	977

EIGHTEENTH DAY

BREAKFAST:
                                      CALORIES

½ cup pineapple juice	60
½ cup puffed rice, with	42
½ cup skim milk	45
Coffee, 1 teaspoon sugar	18

LUNCHEON:

*Sardine Puff (Page 87)	134
*Asparagus Salad (Page 71)	31
Coffee or tea, 1 teaspoon sugar	18

DINNER:

*Cold Fruit Soup (Page 16)	84
*Savory Meat Loaf (Page 41)	283
*Green Beans Parmesan (Page 53)	33
*Stewed Tomatoes (Page 61)	36
*Quick-And-Easy Coffee Cake (Page 104)	129
Coffee or tea, 1 teaspoon sugar	18
	931

NINETEENTH DAY

	CALORIES
BREAKFAST:	
½ cup orange juice	60
1 soft boiled egg	80
1 slice toast	60
Coffee, 1 teaspoon sugar	18

LUNCHEON:

*Broiled Fillet of Sole With Cheese Sauce (Page 29)	132
Lettuce Wedge, with	10
*Raw Vegetable Dip (Page 10)	27
Coffee or tea, 1 teaspoon sugar	18

DINNER:

*Cheese Puffs (2) (Page 9)	56
½ cup tomato juice	25
*Chicken Luau (Page 34)	235
*Zucchini With Fresh Lemon Butter (Page 59)	47
½ cup rice, cooked	100
*Sparkling Pear Dessert (Page 92)	93
Coffee or tea, 1 teaspoon sugar	18
	979

TWENTIETH DAY

BREAKFAST:
CALORIES

½ grapefruit	75
1 slice toast, topped with	60
1 slice American cheese	105
Coffee, 1 teaspoon sugar	18

LUNCHEON:

*Swiss Clam Bun (Page 89)	116
Tomato slices	30
Coffee or tea, 1 teaspoon sugar	18

DINNER:

*Strawberry-Melon Cocktail (Page 8)	39
*Sweet Steak (Page 38)	349
*Broiled Mushrooms (Page 59)	28
½ cup green beans	15
Baked potato	90
*Mapled Pears (Page 99)	35
Coffee or tea, 1 teaspoon sugar	18
	996

TWENTY-FIRST DAY

BREAKFAST:
                                                                  CALORIES

½ fresh orange, sliced	37
*Strawberry Sour Cream Omelet (Page 80)	180
Coffee, 1 teaspoon sugar	18

LUNCHEON:

*Grilled Cheese & Tomato (Page 86)	152
Coffee or tea, 1 teaspoon sugar	18

DINNER:

*Cocktail Onion Appetizers (10) (Page 11)	20
½ cup tomato juice	25
*Broiled Lamb Chops Italienne (Page 44)	345
*Zucchini-Mushroom Duet (Page 63)	46
½ cup carrots	20
*Lemon Sponge Cake (Page 103)	113
Coffee or tea, 1 teaspoon sugar	18
	992

Acorn Squash:
  Baked 60
  Rings with Peas 61
Angel Cake, Lemon 102
Appetizers 7-14
Apples, Baked 96
Apple Beets 55
Applesauce Meringue 107
Apricot Fluff 93
Artichoke, Potted Chicken with 33
Asparagus:
  au Gratin 50
  Bisque 16
  Salad 71
  Sandwich Puff 88
  Spear Salad Mold 78
  Vinaigrette 50
  with Eggs 83

Bacon and Egg Divan 90
Banana:
  Ambrosia 8
  Sole Amandine 28
Barbecue Broiled Chicken 32
Barbecue Sauce, Broiled Swordfish with 27

Barbecued Spareribs 48
Beans:
  Green Parmesan 53
  Green Polynesian 51
  Green and Tomatoes 52
  Green Zippy 51
  Marinated 52
Beef:
  Boiled with Dill Sauce 41
  Egg Drop Soup 20
  Roulades 42
Beefwich, Open-Faced 86
Beets, Apple 55
Beet Borsch 21
Bisque:
  Asparagus 16
  Crabmeat 16
Bouillon, Tomato 18
Boiled Beef with Dill Sauce 41
Bran Muffins, Low-Fat 108
Broccoli Chiffon 54
Broiled:
  Barbecue Chicken 32
  Fillet of Sole with Cheese Sauce 29
  Fish Parmesan (Flounder) 30

INDEX

Grapefruit 8
Lamb Chops, Italienne 44
Mushrooms 59
Scampi 24
Swordfish with Barbecue Sauce 27
Tomatoes with Dill 61
Broth, Vegetable-Clam 19
Brunswick Stew 30
Brussels Sprouts 55
  Dilly Brussels Sprouts 54
Burgers:
  Herbed 40
  Tuna 90

Cabbage:
  Crisp Buttered 56
  Sweet and Sour 56
  Sweet and Sour Red 55
Cakes:
  Coffee Sponge 102
  Lemon Angel 102
  Lemon Sponge 103
  Orange Sponge 103
  Quick and Easy Coffee 104
  Walnut Sponge Roll 104
Calorie Chart 109-124
Canapes:
  Cheese Puffs 9
  Crab 9
  Saltine Pizzas 12
Carrots:
  Herbed 57
  Parsley 57
  with Pineapple 57
  Sesame Slaw 72
Cauliflower:
  with Cheese 58
  Salad 74
Celery Seed Dressing 66
Cheese:
  Puffs 9
  Sauce on Fillet of Sole 29
  and Tomato, Grilled 86

Treat 86
Chicken:
  Baked in Foil 33
  Barbecue Broiled 32
  Brunswick Stew 30
  Luau 34
  Oriental Kabobs 34
  Oven-Fried Parmesan 32
  Potted with Artichoke 33
  Rosemary 35
Chicken Liver:
  Kabobs 31
  Mandarin 31
Chocolate Cream Roll 106
Chops:
  Broiled Lamb Italienne 44
  Sweet and Sour Lamb 43
Chowder, Corn 18
Clam Bun, Swiss 89
Clam-Vegetable Broth 19
Cobbler, Peach Pie 106
Cockaleekie Soup 21
Cocktail:
  Franks in Zesty Sauce 11
  Onion Appetizers 11
  Strawberry-Melon 8
Coconut Meringue Cookies 107
Coffee Cake:
  Quick and Easy 104
  Sponge 102
Colorful Cole Slaw 73
Consomme, Sherry 20
Cookies:
  Coconut Meringue 107
  Cranberry 108
Corn:
  Chowder 18
  Relish Mold 78
  and Tomatoes, Baked 58
Cottage Cheese Omelet 84
Crab Canapes 9
Crabmeat:
  Bisque 16
  Divan 24

INDEX

Crabwich, Deviled 87
Cranberry:
  Cookies 108
  Vegetable Salad Mold 75
Cucumber:
  Cream Broiled Fillets 29
  Egg Wafers 13
  Pickled with Dill 75
  Pineapple Ring 76
  Sticks with Smoked Salmon 10
Curried Lamb Stew 44

Desserts 91-100
Diane, Steak 42
Dill Sauce, Boiled Beef with 41
Dips:
  Raw Vegetable 10
  Zesty for Cocktail Franks 11
Dressing for Salad see Salad Dressing

Egg see also Omelets
  with Asparagus 83
  Beef Drop Soup 20
  Florentine 81
  Puffed 80
  in Tomatoes 82
Egg Salad Mold 83
Eggs 79-84
Entrees 23-48

Fish 23-40 (see also name of fish)
Flank Steak:
  Stuffed 49
  Teriyaki 37
Flounder:
  Broiled Parmesan 30
  Cucumber-Cream Broiled Fillets 29
  Florentine 28
Franks, Cocktail in Zesty Sauce 11
French Onion Soup 22
Fruit:
  Ambrosia 97

Compote 96
  Salad Dressing 66
  Salad Dressing, Extra Low Calorie 68
  Salad Mold 76
  Soup, Cold 16
Gazpacho 18
Grape Fluff 92
Grapefruit:
  Broiled 8
  Ginger Mold 68
Green Beans:
  Island Green Beans 53
  Parmesan 53
  Polynesian 51
  and Tomatoes 52
  Zippy 51
Green Peppers with Tomatoes, Baked 62
Grilled Cheese and Tomato 87
Gumbo, Shrimp 17

Herb-Baked Turkey Roll 36
Herb Dressing 67
Herbed:
  Burgers 40
  Carrots 57

Italian Dressing 66

Jellied Tomato Soup with Sherry 19

Kabobs:
  Chicken Liver 31
  Oriental Chicken 34
Kraut Relish 72

Lamb:
  Chops, Broiled Italienne 44
  Chops, Sweet and Sour 43
  Leg of, au Café 46
  Leg of, Jardiniere 45
  Shanks à l'Orange 45

149

INDEX

Stew, Curried 44
Lemon:
  Angel Cake 102
  Angel Fluff 94
  French Dressing 67
  Ice 95
  Sponge Cake 103
Mandarin Salad 69
Marinade, Steak 36
Marinated Beans 52
Meat Loaf:
  Savory 41
  Zesty 39
Meatball Stew 40
Menus 125-146
Minute Steak, Savory 43
Mongol, Puree Soup 20
Muffins, Low-Fat Bran 108
Mushrooms:
  Broiled 59
  Omelet 81
  Salad 69
  Savory Stuffed 13
  Zucchini Duet 64

Omelet:
  Cottage Cheese 84
  Mushroom 81
  Ranch 84
  Strawberry Sour Cream 80
  Zucchini 82
Onion:
  Cocktail Appetizers 11
  Soup, French 22
Orange:
  Freeze 12
  Nugget Roast Turkey 35
  Snow 92
  Spinach Salad Bowl 70
  Sponge Cake 103
Oriental Chicken Kabobs 34
Oriental Spinach Soup 22
Oven-Fried Chicken Parmesan 32

Parmesan:
  Broiled Tomatoes 62
  Green Beans 53
  Oven-Fried Chicken 32
  Zucchini 64
Peach Cobbler Pie 106
Pears:
  in Claret 98
  in Gin 98
  Mapled 99
  Melba 98
  Sparkling Dessert 92
Pickled Cucumbers with Dill 75
Pie:
  Peach Cobbler 106
  Pears Helene 105
  Raspberry Chiffon 105
Pineapple:
  Cucumber Ring 76
  Grape Sherbet 94
Pizza:
  American 88
  Saltine 12
Poached Salmon 21
Polynesian Green Beans 51
Potted Chicken with Artichoke 33
Puree Mongol Soup 20

Raspberry Chiffon Pie 105
Raw Vegetable Dip 10
Relish, Kraut 72
Rice:
  Orange 59
  Pineapple 59
  Tomato Soup 17
Roast Veal, Savory 48
Roulades, Beef 42

Salads 65-78
Salad Dressing:
  Celery Seed 66
  Extra Low Calorie for Fruit Cup 68

INDEX

for Fruit Salad 66
Herb 67
Italian 66
Lemon French 67
Salad Molds 75-78
Salmon:
  on the Halfshell 89
  Poached 27
  Smoked with Cucumber Sticks 10
Saltine Pizzas 12
Sardine Puff 87
Sauce:
  Barbecue with Broiled Swordfish 27
  Cheese with Broiled Fillet of Sole 29
  Dill with Boiled Beef 41
Scallop Bites 14
Scallopini, Veal 47
Scampi, Broiled 24
Shanks, Lamb à l'Orange 45
Sherry Ambrosia 95
  Consomme 20
  Jellied Tomato Soup with 19
Shrimp:
  Baked Stuffed 25
  Broiled Scampi 24
  Deluxe Salad 71
  Gumbo 17
  Kabobs 14
  Newburg 26
  Sauté 25
  Stew 26
Smoked Salmon-Cucumber Sticks 10
Sole:
  Banana Amandine 28
  Broiled Fillet with Cheese Sauce 29
Soups 15-22
Spare Ribs, Barbecued 48
Spinach:
  Creamed 60
  Orange Salad Bowl 70
  Salad 70
  Soup 19
Sponge Cake:
  Coffee 102
  Lemon 103
  Orange 103
  Walnut 104
Squash, Acorn:
  Baked 60
  Rings with Peas 61
Steak:
  Diane 42
  Flank Burgundy 38
  Marinade 36
  Savory, Minute 43
  Stuffed Flank 39
  Sweet 38
  Swiss 37
  Teriyaki 37
Stew:
  Brunswick 30
  Curried Lamb 44
  Meatball 40
Strawberry:
  Flip 96
  Melon Cocktail 8
  Sour Cream Omelet 80
Stroganoff, Veal 46
Sweet and Sour:
  Cabbage 56
  Lamb Chops 43
  Red Cabbage 55
Sweet Steak 38
Swiss Steak 37
Swordfish, Broiled with Barbecue Sauce 27

Teriyaki, Flank Steak 37
Tomato:
  Aspic 77
  Bouillon 18

INDEX

Broiled with Dill 61
Broiled Parmesan 62
Cheesewich 87
and Corn, baked 58
Corn Creole 63
Eggs in 82
and Green Beans 62
Green Peppers, baked with 62
Rice Soup 17
Soup with Sherry, Jellied 19
Spanish Cream 97
Stewed 61
Tuna Burger 90
Turkey:
  Herb-Baked Roll 36
  Orange-Nugget Roast 35

Veal:
  Roast 48
  Sauté 47
  Scallopini 47
  Stroganoff 46

Vegetable:
  Clam Broth 19
  Raw Dip 10
  Salad Bowl 74
  Salad Mold 77
Vegetables 49-64 (*see also* name of vegetable)

Walnut Sponge Roll 104

Yogurt:
  Citrus Flavored 99
  Ginger 99
  Maple-Nut 100
  Spiced Honey 100

Zucchini:
  with Lemon Butter 63
  Mushroom Duet 64
  Omelet 82
  Parmesan 64